One Hundred Years of the British Fire Engine

One Hundred Years of the British Fire Engine

Neil Wallington

JEREMY MILLS
PUBLISHING LIMITED

First published in 2008 by Jeremy Mills Publishing

ISBN 978-1-906600-28-0 (hardback)
ISBN 978-1-906600-30-3 (paperback)

Front cover, top: A fine parade of London Fire Brigade Leyland fire engines outside Shoreditch fire station, Tabernacle Street, EC2, circa 1924. On the far right is a 50ft pump escape, carrying a 50ft wooden wheeled escape ladder, whilst the other two are both pumps. All three fire engines are still on solid tyres with the crew on minimal seating on each side. (London Fire Brigade)

Front cover, below: The awesome power of uncontrolled fire is well shown in this image of West Yorkshire firefighters getting to work at the scene of a huge blaze in a disused mill at Bradford in 1999. Note the aerial ladder platform in the background. (Brian Saville, West Yorkshire Fire Service)

Frontispiece: A head-on view of a truly immaculate AEC Merryweather 100ft turntable ladder formerly delivered new to Croydon Fire Brigade in 1963. This fire engine was absorbed along with the fleets of nine individual brigades into the enlarged London Fire Brigade (LFB) at the inception of the Greater London Council in 1965. After being finally retired from operational service in the early 1990's, CBY 1 was preserved by the LFB as a classic working example of its time and today this turntable ladder is in regular use at fire service charity events and other functions. (Paul Wood)

Contents

	Foreword by Sir Ken Knight	vi
	Introduction	vii
ONE	A Historical Overview	1
TWO	The Motor's Here To Stay	9
THREE	Coming In From The Cold	15
FOUR	Prelude To War	24
FIVE	The Blitz And The Coming Of The National Fire Service	33
SIX	The Road To Recovery	41
SEVEN	The Phoenix Arises: The Auxiliary Fire Service Returns	48
EIGHT	Innovation: Large And Small	57
NINE	New Versus Tried And Trusted	65
TEN	Competition Takes Its Toll	74
ELEVEN	Towards The End Of The Century	82
TWELVE	New Concepts, New Ideas And Fresh Challenges	92
	Acknowledgements	116
	Further Reading	117
	Index	118

Foreword
by Sir Ken Knight CBE, QFSM, DL
Government Chief Fire and Rescue Adviser

Right from the time that human beings first discovered fire, it became necessary to find the means of tackling flames whenever they got out of control. The first organised yet primitive attempts at firefighting began during the time of the Roman Empire, but it was not until the seventeenth century that firefighting methods began to be developed.

This progress led to the emergence of the first manually pumped fire engines, pulled at first by hand, then drawn by horses. The subsequent arrival of steam powered fire engines revolutionised firefighting capability, and the coming of the internal combustion engine saw a new age bringing new shape and style as well as improved technical features to firefighting vehicles.

Fire engines are probably some of the most impressive and dramatic vehicles to be seen on the road today, especially when they are responding to an emergency, and the story of the development of British fire engines is without doubt a fascinating tale that reflects challenges, success, and not a few misfortunes along the way. It is also true to say that over the past century, fire brigades have played a significant part in the steady emergence of new designs and engineering features of ladder-carrying pumps, turntable ladders, rescue tenders and a wide range of other fire engines.

The vast social change witnessed by today's world, and increasing technology at both work and home, together with more potentially harmful products in use in industry and commerce, has widened the scope of the emergency response work of the British fire service. Over the past decades, the demands of non-fire accident-type rescue work have also steadily increased. This is all reflected in the various types of fire engine in use in the modern day fire service. The operating capabilities and features of today's fire engines would surely amaze the brave brass-helmeted firemen who went to tackle fires clinging aboard those first stuttering and slow open motorised pumps of 100 years ago.

In his latest book, Neil Wallington is to be congratulated in setting out the story of the development of British fire engines in such an interesting and informative manner. I commend this book to all those who have an interest in the work of the British fire service and of the men and women who form the front-line of the nation's defence against the ever-present ravages of fire.

Introduction

May I firstly clearly state that this book is not intended to be an absolutely definitive history of every make of fire engine ever to leave a British factory. It is instead rather a personal celebration and general overview of the significant events over a period of 100 years concerning the origins, development and, sadly, the numerical demise of the all-British fire engine in recent decades.

During the early years of my fire service career, I spent some time as a turnout driver of the London Fire Brigade in the busy West End of London, and had the pleasure of handling a few of what would today be regarded as 'classic' fire engines.

These included what I considered several of the finest of that time, the petrol Rolls Royce-powered Dennis F12 and the AEC Regent III Merryweather pumps. Both these fire engines were very different in their ways. The F12 had unprecedented acceleration for a fire engine of that era: 0 to 60mph in 45 seconds. However, stopping an F12 with its somewhat basic servo-braking system could be interesting, especially on wet roads.

The AEC Regent's diesels were, by comparison, lumbering giants with a constant mesh gearbox that could occasionally be a real nightmare. Strangely though, most LFB drivers seemed to fall in love with the AECs – somehow they never let you forget that they were built on a bus chassis.

Probably my all-time favourite was the Dennis F101, the first British fire engine to be powered by a Rolls Royce diesel engine. These were truly beautiful machines both to the eye and to drive; their five-speed close-ratio gearbox was an absolute revelation to use and the F101 engine's output made them a delight to drive. It is pleasing to see that examples of all three have survived into active preservation.

This book chronicles the early days of the motorised age, the many progressive developments in style and technical engineering, the dramatic years of World War II where the fire service and its engines really was in the front line, and the post-war influence on the new fire engines of the 1950s and 1960s. Then came the emergence of high rise aerial firefighting vehicles and other specialist tenders directly as a result of the expanding emergency workload of the fire service. This work included a growing variety of non-fire rescue work such as road and other transport crashes where persons were trapped, and accidents involving hazardous and toxic chemicals.

The later chapters leading up to modern times and the new century also relate to the virtual end of the 'complete' British fire engine from a single manufacturer, and the consequential increasing use of various European chassis as the base for today's new gleaming and technological fire engines.

Finally, I must pay my own tribute to the firefighting and rescue crews who man today's fire engines at fire stations up and down the country, from those in high-risk city centre fire stations to those who cover large rural areas with their consequential dangers. Wherever they serve, British firefighters and their fire engines form the nation's premier and selfless emergency service. I trust that this modest book underlines some interesting aspects of the past 100 years in both peacetime and war, and provides an insight into just how resolute and professional the British fire service has been in past times and undoubtedly continues to be as it faces the wide and varied challenges of the modern era.

Neil Wallington
Bourne, Lincolnshire
August 2008

CHAPTER ONE

A Historical Overview

At the end of the 19th century horse-drawn steam power was at its peak in fire brigades. The two predominant British steam fire pump manufacturers, Merryweather and Shand Mason, had between them captured the home market, together with many orders from overseas brigades.

However, against the background of increasing availability of the internal combustion engine, Merryweather produced their first self-propelled Fire King model in 1899. This had a 30 hp two-cylinder steam engine providing power for both road propulsion and fire pump. Unfortunately, the Fire King weighed in at nearly six tons and, with a 12 mph maximum road speed, it is hardly surprising that fire chiefs looked towards the petrol engine to provide the way ahead.

In 1901, Liverpool Fire Brigade converted a 24 hp Daimler chassis to carry a 60-gallon water tank linked by pipework to a cylinder of carbonic gas. Firefighting water was discharged through one-inch hose reel tubing on a rear-mounted rotating drum. However, contemporary evidence suggests that the Liverpool Daimler conversion was a temperamental and unreliable starter and before long it was replaced by an electric vehicle.

Around this time several other brigades, the first being Eccles in Lancashire, commissioned motor tenders that were simply light passenger cars such as the 7 hp, two-cylinder Bijou. In fire brigade use it was soon evident that these early cars were simply not sturdy or powerful enough to serve as proper fire engines.

THE FIRST BRITISH MOTOR PROPELLED FIRE ENGINE

Finchley Fire Brigade's 1904 Merryweather, now in the Science Museum collection. (Author's collection)

Thus it was that around 1902 Superintendent Eddington of Tottenham Fire Brigade in North London produced an outline design for a bespoke motorised fire engine. Eddington's specification called for a petrol engined vehicle able to carry a 50 ft wheeled wooden escape ladder and have an inbuilt 60-gallon chemical extinguisher fed through hose reel tubing on a rotating drum. An order was placed with Merryweather's to build the vehicle, and in 1903 Tottenham Fire Brigade proudly took delivery of the first British motor-propelled fire engine. The historic Tottenham Merryweather was powered by a four-cylinder, 30 hp Aster engine and was housed in a new fire station specifically designed with the motor age in mind rather than the stabling and other needs of horse-drawn fire engines.

Not to be outdone, Chief Officer Sly of the nearby Finchley Brigade also had plans for a motorised pump and in 1904 his brigade took delivery of a similar Merryweather/Aster. Like the Tottenham vehicle, Finchley's Merryweather also carried a wooden wheeled escape ladder and chemical extinguisher. However, the true significance of Finchley's new fire engine was that it was the first to have its fire pump driven by a power take-off from the road engine. The pump delivered 500 gallons per minute and it also carried 180 ft of canvas delivery hose. The Finchley Merryweather was the world's first truly self-contained motorised pumping fire engine and is today part of the Science Museum collection in London.

BRIGHT SPARK

It is also interesting to note that between 1902 and 1913, the London Brigade had a flirtation with battery electric-driven pumps. These were the product of the Cedes Electric Traction company, makers of early trolleybuses. Merryweather also produced a similar electric model. Sadly, at a time when the new motor pumps were showing themselves to be increasingly reliable and powerful, the two-ton deadweight of batteries under the bonnet of the electric pumps together with their problems of battery maintenance soon sounded their death knell.

DENNIS ENTERS THE FRAY

One emerging company of this time was to soon become a major player on the British fire engine scene. The Dennis Brothers company started life in a small shop at Guildford in Surrey in 1895, first manufacturing bicycles before expanding into motor powered tricycles and then cars. The two founding Dennis brothers, John and Raymond, built their first fire engine in 1908. This was a pump for the City of Bradford Fire Brigade that cost the princely sum of £900. Powered by a White & Poppe 60 hp engine with a four-speed gearbox, it had a power take-off that drove a Gwynne-Sargent centrifugal pump.

The Bradford Dennis naturally attracted a lot of attention from other fire brigades at a time when motorised fire engines were increasingly replacing steam and horse-drawn pumps. In 1910 the London Brigade placed a significant order for the same Dennis model as Bradford's, thus beginning a long lasting relationship between the company and the capital's fire brigade. The early London Dennis motor pumps had solid rubber tyres with steel studded fabric wraps to combat the risk of skidding on wet tramlines.

LEYLAND JOINS IN

The other major British fire engine manufacturer of the first half of the century was the infant Leyland company of Chorley in Lancashire. In 1910, the company produced the first of many hundreds of Leyland motor fire engines when they delivered a pump to Dublin Fire Brigade. This was powered by an 85 hp six-cylinder petrol engine.

A preserved 1936 Dennis Big 4 pump escape of the London Fire Brigade, one of a batch of eight commissioned that year. The LFB specified transverse crew seats and classified these vehicles as dual purpose, for they were able to carry a 50 ft wheeled escape, as here, or a 35 ft extension ladder. BYV 306 served right through the London Blitz and was finally taken out of service in 1956. (Author's collection)

By World War I, other manufacturers including Albion, Argyle, Commer-Simonis, Halley and John Morris were all producing various types of motorised pumps. However by the 1920s Dennis and Leyland were already dominating the fire engine market. Merryweather too remained active, although the company had persisted with chain drive until 1926, when they started using Albion chassis carrying the Merryweather badge.

THE FIRST TL
Special appliances other than pumping fire engines had started to appear quite early on. In 1908, Merryweather built the first British turntable ladder (TL). Although its 65 ft ladder sections were constructed of wood, the mechanical drive to extend, raise and rotate the ladders was powered from the road engine. Two years later, Leyland delivered two foam tenders to the London Fire Brigade, whilst in 1918 Dennis built two breathing apparatus tenders for London.

TECHNOLOGY MOVES ON
Over the next two decades up to World War II, the principal developments in fire engine design included larger and more powerful engines, improved suspension and braking systems, pneumatic tyres and turntable ladders with welded steel ladder sections capable of reaching up to heights of 100 ft and more.

Bodywork styles also underwent continual improvement. From the beginning of the motor age, crews continued to stand or be seated down either side of the fire engine, hanging on and trying to get rigged in uniform as best they could. This was obviously a hazardous process when the machine was en route to a fire, especially as the fire engines would be travelling at higher speeds than in horse-drawn days. If the driver suddenly swerved or braked, firemen were often thrown off, with resultant serious injury or even death. Furthermore in winter months, the crew would often arrive at an incident already soaking wet or frozen through.

To combat this serious danger, in 1933 Dennis introduced their New World style of bodywork where the crew rode within the body itself, entering from the rear of the fire engine. One year later, Dennis was offering a transverse seating arrangement for the fire crew behind the driver and officer in charge. In the early 1930s, Dennis, Leyland and Merryweather all produced examples of all-enclosed limousine type fire engine bodies on various special appliances such as emergency tenders, but within several years the first limousine pumps also began to appear.

Leyland concentrated particularly on its turntable ladder production and with a new franchise with the German company Metz in place, a

Now in preservation, HB 7231 is a 1952 AEC Regent III/ Merryweather pump escape of Merthyr Tydfil Fire Brigade, one of a number of AEC fire engines that went into service during the 1950s in various fire brigades. (Jerry Hepworth)

From the 1950s, the number of special appliances in operational service steadily grew, both in number and sophistication. 4999 SC was a 1963 AEC Mercury/Merryweather emergency tender of South Eastern Fire Brigade, Scotland, operating from Lauriston Place Fire Station, Edinburgh. (Jerry Hepworth)

number of new TLs went into service with British city brigades until the onset of war brought this successful technical marriage to an end. Although most of these Leylands were 100 ft, 101 ft or 104 ft versions, a 150 ft Leyland/Metz six-section TL went into service with Hull City Police Fire Brigade in 1936. At the time, this was the tallest TL in the world.

AFTER WWII

The years of World War II saw the nationalisation of the fire service (1941), by which time British fire engine fleets had been supplemented by the addition of hundreds of government-supplied motor pumps (including Fordson, Bedford and Dodge models), together with trailer pumps, turntable ladders and various special appliances to combat the threat of aerial raiding. History recalls that little realistic fire engine development took place until the denationalisation of the fire service in 1948. However, one major advance of this time was the introduction of a standard set of technical specifications for various types of British fire engine.

From the 1950s there was a steady expansion of chassis types designed for fire engine use, in local authority, industrial and airfield applications. Dennis in particular quickly reasserted its place as the market leader with several completely new models. These included the F8 water tender and the F7 (both of 1949) and the subsequent shorter wheelbase F12 model. Other early chassis makes to arrive on the post-war fire engine scene included AEC (Regent Series III), Albion (CX), Bedford (S, A and J types), Commer (QX and Karrier Gamecock) and the Leyland Comet. Later arrivals included the ERF (1967), Ford, Dodge and Shelvoke & Drewry.

Not long after the arrival of the Mark I Land Rover in 1948 came the first light pump for rural off-road firefighting based upon the Solihull

4 x 4. Similarly, when the Range Rover arrived some 20 years later, the Carmichael 6 x 4 version was soon a popular choice for fast response emergency/rescue tenders for the increasing amount of road accident work attended by fire brigades.

NEW BODY BUILDERS

The range of post-war specialist fire engine bodybuilders included such companies as Alfred Miles, Angloco, Carmichael, Cheshire Fire Engineering (CFE), Hampshire Car Bodies (HCB), David Haydon, John Morris, James Whitson and Wilsden.

Engineering landmarks of the post-war fire engine era included the first use of the diesel engine, the first automatic gearbox on a British fire engine (the Dennis F24 of 1956), the ready availability of power steering, the increasing use of glass fibre bodywork and the ultimate introduction of steel crew safety cabs with a tilting option.

However, several models of considerable technological promise never attracted enough commercial support to be commercially viable. In 1958 Leyland reappeared in the fire marketplace with their Firemaster model. This was based upon a flat chassis frame with a 9.8-litre diesel engine mounted amidships, with semi-automatic transmission and a front mounted pump. Sadly the interest in the Firemaster never transferred into firm orders and only 10 of these innovative Leylands were ever built.

By the early 1960s, hydraulic platforms were beginning to make their appearance in British fire brigades. An example of the new breed of aerial fire engines is BEX 812C, Great Yarmouth Fire Brigade's 1965 Simon SS 65-footer, mounted upon a Bedford TKEL chassis with bodywork by HCB Angus. Great Yarmouth was absorbed into Norfolk Fire Brigade in 1974 and BEX 812C was finally retired in 1982.
(Jerry Hepworth)

HYDRAULICS ARRIVE

The development of post-war aerial fire engines in the late 1950s saw hydraulic power being used for all ladder evolutions on Merryweather TLs. Up to then, British brigades had used the TL exclusively for high-rise firefighting and rescue although hydraulic platforms had been successfully introduced elsewhere in the world, particularly in the USA.

The first British hydraulic platform (HP) was commissioned by Monmouthshire Fire Brigade in 1963. This was a Simon SS 65 ft twin-boomed machine mounted upon a Commer VAC chassis. This pioneering fire engine was soon to be followed by other HPs and, over the next 20 years, technology saw the operating field of TLs and HPs coming together to produce the first aerial ladder platform (ALPs).

FOREIGN INTERVENTION

The 1980s also brought the first use of a Volvo chassis (the FL 614) for water tender use and from then on, the prominence of the British fire engine was under some international challenge. Before long more Volvos, together with Mercedes, Scania, and MAN fire engines had started to become widespread in the front line, although mostly with bodywork and fire engineering by British companies. Regretfully, despite its proud and long history, the classic all-British fire engine was destined to become a memory of the nostalgic past.

This 1977 ERF 84RF (TCA 836R) with bodywork by Cheshire Fire Engineering served with Cheshire Fire Brigade and is seen here attending a lorry fire on a motorway. ERF first produced a chassis for fire service application some 10 years earlier. (Author's collection)

CHAPTER TWO

The Motor's Here To Stay

The first decade of the 20th century was a time of continual experimentation and development for a number of fire brigades, both large and small, as they increasingly worked with the early commercial vehicle manufacturers to adapt the internal combustion engine for fire service work.

FIRST INNOVATIVE ATTEMPTS

Even before the turn of the century, there had been several attempts to couple a petrol engine to drive a reciprocating fire pump. One of the earliest British examples was that of 1895 for the Hon. Evelyn Ellis, for his private estate fire brigade in Datchet in Buckinghamshire. This consisted of a trailer-mounted Daimler engine that drove a single cylinder pump via a belt drive.

By the turn of the century, the use of motorised vehicles was gathering pace. In 1901, Liverpool Fire Brigade converted a 24 hp Daimler chassis to carry a 60-gallon water tank linked to a cylinder of carbonic gas that discharged water through hose reel tubing. In the same year, the Eccles Brigade in Lancashire were the first of several brigades to adapt early car chassis, such as the Bijou, for fire service use. Despite its modest 7 hp engine, the Bijou managed to carry a crew of five plus the driver, together with a ladder, some hose and extinguishers. The Metropolitan (London) Fire Brigade also tried several Stanley steam cars to transport senior officers.

FIRST PROPER FIRE ENGINES

However, truly bespoke motorised fire engines specifically built for firefighting were not long in arriving. In 1903, the Merryweather company built their first petrol-engined fire appliance to the order of the Tottenham Brigade in north London. This utilised a 30 hp Aster and carried a 50 ft wooden wheeled escape ladder and was believed to be the world's first motor-driven escape. Less than a year later, Merryweather's supplied the neighbouring Finchley Brigade with an Aster powered pump escape. Finchley were able to claim this vehicle to be the world's first motor fire engine supplied to a public fire brigade to have its 250 gpm (gallons per minute) fire pump driven by the road engine.

MERRYWEATHER LEADS THE WAY

The London-based Merryweather company had been building manual pumps since the 18th century and horse-drawn steam pumps since the 1850s for home and overseas customers. In 1899 Merryweather built their first self-propelled steam pump, the Fire King. 24 of these had been delivered to British fire brigades by the outbreak of World War I. Not unsurprisingly, in the face of the increasing reliability and power of the motor fire engine, the attraction of the Fire King began to fade.

LEYLAND'S FIRST FIRE PUMP

The Leyland Motor company of Chorley, Lancashire, was formed in 1907 and the company delivered their first fire engine in 1910. This was built to the order of the Dublin Fire Department. Described as a 'high-speed' motor pump, it was constructed on what became the U type chassis and was powered by a six-cylinder petrol engine rated at 85 hp. On trial in Dublin it is reputed to have reached 60 mph. The Dublin Leyland had shaft drive, solid tyres, and a gearbox power take-off to drive the rear-mounted Mather & Platt 250 gpm centrifugal fire pump. So well built was this original Leyland that it was still in service in 1939, by which time it had been fitted with pneumatic tyres. The demand for Leyland fire appliances was so great that in 1913 the company opened a new plant at Chorley solely devoted to fire engine production. *(Dennis Fire)*

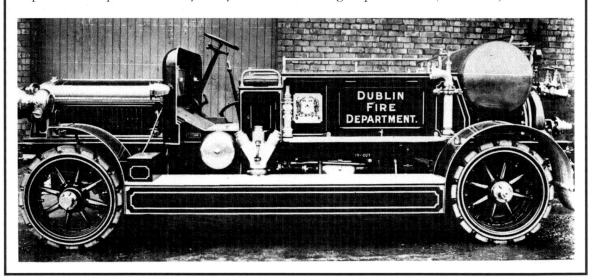

A chain drive Merryweather Hatfield pump of the London Fire Brigade, pictured in 1909 at Southwark HQ. Note the long suction hose with strainer at its end for working from open water supplies. (London Fire Brigade)

By 1916, Merryweather took a commercial decision to move exclusively into the motorised market as increasing enquiries were received from city and urban fire brigades who wanted to dispense with steam and adopt motor power. Interestingly, Merryweather's major 19th-century British steam competitor, Shand Mason, resisted the temptation to move into complete motorisation. As late as 1913, Shand Mason was still experimenting with fitting one of their steam pumps onto the rear of a Daimler motor chassis. Shand Mason was finally taken over by Merryweather in 1922.

MAJOR MAKERS EMERGE

The end of the first decade of the 20th century saw the emergence of two significant fire engine builders, Dennis and Leyland. Collectively, the two makes rapidly grew to dominate the British fire engine commercial scene during the years until the Second World War.

Other British commercial vehicle manufacturers who also turned their hand to building fire engines during the early years included Albion, Argyle, Belsize, Commer-Simonis, Halley, Kelly and Tilling-Stevens. However, such was the rapid market domination of

THE FIRST DENNIS FIRE ENGINES

The first fire engine to bear the Dennis badge was supplied to Bradford Fire Brigade in 1908. Until then, Dennis had used Aster engines in their cars and vans, but their first fire engine was powered by a White & Poppe four-cylinder engine boasting 45 hp. The cost of this historic Dennis was £900. Two years later, the London Fire Brigade (LFB) purchased its first Dennis pumps, beginning a relationship that was to last for over 50 years. These first LFB Dennis pumps had four-cylinder 40 hp engines and rear-mounted 250 gpm Gwynne centrifugal pumps. Up to the outbreak of war in 1939, Dennis had supplied 261 fire engines to the capital's fire brigade.

Dennis and Leyland, that many other early fire engine manufacturers simply turned their attention back towards producing other commercial vehicles, whilst some simply disappeared from the scene.

FIRE ENGINEERING

Alongside the developing fire engine manufacturing methods and steady improvements in overall performance during the early part of the 20th century, there were also significant improvements in fire engineering. For some years, Merryweather had produced their Hatfield reciprocating three-cylinder water pumps, although right from the start, Dennis used the more efficient centrifugal (or turbine) fire pump developed by Gwynne of Chiswick in their first fire engines.. In 1921, Dennis turned to using Italian Tamini centrifugal pumps on their fire engines and before long were manufacturing their own Dennis brand fire pumps at their Guildford factory based upon the Tamini design.

Although many country and parish brigades still relied upon horse-drawn steamers, in 1914 Belfast is believed to have been the first city fire brigade to become completely motorised in its front line fire vehicles. In the country areas, many rural and parish fire brigades still continued to rely upon horse-drawn steamers, partly due to the cost of motor fire engines, although by 1920 the use of horses and steam firefighting power was fast diminishing right across the United Kingdom. The London Fire Brigade finally bade farewell to the last of

Commissioned by the London Fire Brigade in 1919, this Dennis emergency tender was one of the first of its kind, having a prime purpose of providing additional breathing sets, electrical power for floodlighting and various items of rescue equipment. It was based at Clerkenwell Fire Station. Note the 12 mph restriction. (London Fire Brigade)

its specially bred fire horses in 1921; these had pulled a wooden hand-wound turntable ladder at Kensington Fire Station.

TURNTABLE LADDER DEVELOPMENTS

By then, the number of motor fire engines of different types really was growing apace. Although hand-wound turntable ladders (TLs) had been in operational use for around 20 years, a major advance in their early development had come in 1908 when Merryweather built the first TL that derived its drive directly from the road engine to provide power to extend and raise the 65 ft wooden ladder sections. Rotation of the turntable was still carried out by hand. This TL went not to British firefighters, but to Shanghai Fire Brigade.

Various TLs of this time were offered with options that included the ladder sections being powered by a petrol engine, carbon dioxide gas, or compressed air. The LFB preferred German Magirus ladders married to a Tillings-Stevens chassis, whilst several British brigades, including Nottingham and Newcastle, commissioned other Tilling-Stevens petrol electric TLs. In 1922 Morris, who had earlier delivered several gas-powered TLs, stole a march by using a German Magirus 85 ft TL that employed engine power for all three-ladder evolutions (elevation, extension and rotation). The first such Morris/Magirus TL went to Glasgow Fire Brigade. Not to be outdone, Leyland introduced the first German Metz 85 ft TL into the United Kingdom, with the first being sold to Manchester Fire Brigade. All these TLs still featured wooden ladder sections, with steel versions not appearing until 1932.

BODYWORK STYLES

Fire engine bodywork and locker styles were also developing, although the Braidwood style, where the crew sat facing outwards on bench seats or stood down each side of the vehicle, prevailed for another two decades or more, despite fairly regular casualties caused by firemen

---

BUILT TO LAST

The engineering excellence and longevity of some early fire engines is quite remarkable. In 1910, two Dennis motor pumps were delivered to Kingston-upon-Thames Fire Brigade. These went on to serve the area faithfully over the next two decades and more. In 1934 both pumps were returned to the Dennis factory at Guildford for a complete mechanical overhaul. On detailed examination of the two Kingston pumps, it was found that on one of these, none of the engine's original 1910 main and big end bearings, pistons, valves or camshafts required replacement. Even the crankshaft wear did not exceed .003 inch. Records show that the total cost of the entire overhaul and replacements parts for both Kingston's machines was £300.

A 1924 Tilling-Stevens/Foamite foam tender of the London Fire Brigade. (London Fire Brigade)

being flung off en route to an incident. Braidwood bodies continued in vogue until the first inside-body seating arrangement arrived with the introduction in 1928 of Dennis's New World model, although this was still essentially an open fire engine. Firemen crewing pumps continued to be battered by the wind and rain, and simply had to grit their teeth and get on with the job. Although safer inboard seating layouts for crews did become available before World War II, a few open-bodied pumps lasted in operational service right through into the early 1960s.

The earliest limousine bodied pumping fire engines did not appear until 1931, when Edinburgh commissioned their first all-enclosed pump. This was based upon an Albion chassis with bodywork by Merryweather and had seats inside for a crew of up to 12 firemen. By then, a few semi-enclosed specialist fire vehicles had appeared on the scene. As early as 1912, the LFB had commissioned a semi-enclosed Dennis emergency tender. This contained a built-in lighting generator, breathing apparatus, resuscitation equipment and various rescue tools carried inside the van-type body.

Trailer pumps made their first regular appearance in the 1920s and these were particularly useful to rural brigades to readily increase their firefighting waterpower. Dennis produced their very first trailer pump in 1922 using a specially designed multi-stage centrifugal pump, and many thousands subsequently went into service around the world.

TOOLS FOR THE JOB

History records that there were no national technical specifications for fire engines until 1948, when the lessons of wartime firefighting were embodied in the first issue of the Joint Committee for Design and Development specifications, and the subsequent Home Office Standards of Fire Cover that set out certain pre-determined attendances to fires. In the 1920s various fire service associations had starting making recommendations in terms of fire engine power and pumping capability. It was suggested that for high-risk areas of cities, dockland and industrial areas, a 70 hp fire engine with a 1,000 gpm pump output was sufficient. At the other end of the scale in rural areas, a 200 gpm light pump or trailer pump was recommended, with the provision of at least 1,000 ft of hose.

CHAPTER THREE

Coming In From The Cold

By the early 1920s, the widespread use of motorised fire engines in municipal fire brigades in British cities and the larger towns had greatly improved the levels of fire cover provided to the public.

The advent of the motor fire engine meant that response times to fire calls were much reduced compared to horse-drawn days. Motor fire engines carried onboard first-aid firefighting water, usually around 40 to 50 gallons, which enabled the crew to mount an immediate attack using a hose reel on the fire as soon as the fire engine pulled up at the scene of the outbreak.

Even in rural areas, where some steam pumps were still in operational use, the ready availability of motor fire engines and trailer pumps quietly revolutionised firefighting efficiency and effectiveness.

CARRYING IT OFF

Compared to their steam-driven forebears, motorised fire engines were also increasingly able to carry a much greater payload of firefighting and rescue equipment. This included longer and more robust-wheeled escape and extension ladders, hook and scaling ladders, rolled 2.5-inch hose, a variety of water fittings such as dividing and collecting breechings, standpipes and chimney fire gear (rods, tubing and stirrup pump), together with various rescue and general purpose lines.

This was also the time of continual technical development. Key to this was the innovative installation of the fire pump and its power take-off. The water tank and all the necessary fire engineering and plumbing needed to be mounted on a commercial chassis to give a fire engine an efficient and reliable all-round operational performance.

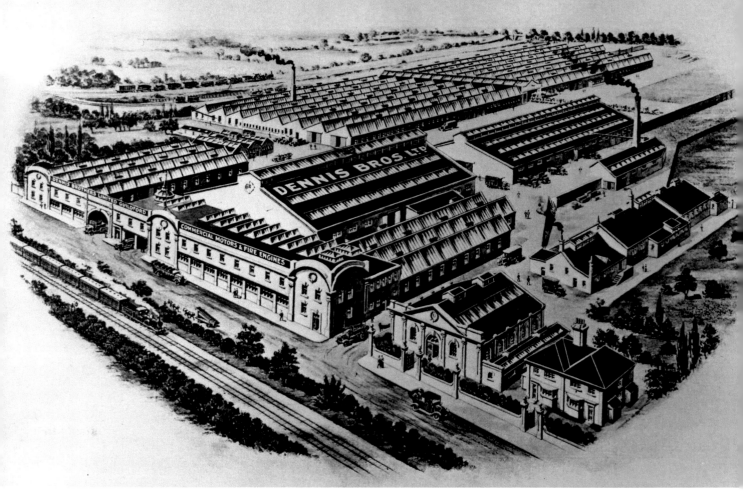

An artist's impression c.1930 of the Dennis Brothers factory at Guildford, Surrey. (Dennis Fire)

There were also newer and growing fire risks to provide for. In 1924, the Merryweather company exhibited a new design of foam tender at the British Empire Exhibition at Wembley. This foam tender embodied the very latest technology for fighting oil and petrol fires that used the chemical reaction between the contents of two separate tanks – one of acid and the other of alkaline – to produce 1,800 gallons of 'Fire Suds' foam. Merryweather seemed to have had a thing about foam because in 1933, they devoted a good deal of time and resources in an unsuccessful attempt to pioneer an onboard system that utilised exhaust gases to generate firefighting foam.

LAYING LOW

In 1928 Dennis built their first fire engine on the company's new low load line passenger chassis that had been launched one year earlier. Designated the G type pump, the frame of this model was only 21 inches off the ground, and this Dennis was an instant success. Powered by a 50 hp, 5.7-litre, four-cylinder engine through a four-speed crash box, the G type had a 145-inch wheelbase, vacuum servo-assisted brakes on all four wheels, and a 300 gpm rear-mounted centrifugal turbine pump.

BRAVE NEW WORLD

The equipment-carrying capacity of a fire engine was to a large extent dictated by the available room within the bodywork style of a particular model. However, with their increasingly powerful engines and ever-faster road speeds, fire engines with the traditional Braidwood body with 'down the side' seating were becoming positively dangerous for fire crews up and down the country. Both Dennis Brothers and Leyland recognised this serious operational difficulty for fire brigades when they introduced their respective New World pumps with wagonette style bodies. In these, the crew entered through the rear and sat safely inside the body of the vehicle.

The first New World Dennis was built in 1928 and was delivered to the order of Luton Fire Brigade. It had a 250 gpm pump mounted underneath the driver's seat, a 40-gallon tank, and carried a 35 ft extension ladder. One year later, Dennis delivered another variant of their New World design to Birmingham Fire Brigade. This was a long wheelbase forward control pump with inside facing seating for a crew of 12 firemen.

Leyland, the other major British fire engine manufacturer of the time, soon followed with their New World models, with three normal control versions going to Birmingham Fire Brigade in 1931. These had 115 bhp, six-cylinder OHV (overhead valve) engines and midships-mounted 500 gpm Rees Returbo pumps.

LEYLAND FKI

By the early 1930s, the Leyland range of pumping fire engines had grown to include the FK1 model with a six-cylinder engine and 400 gpm pump and the low load line FT1 with its more powerful 100 bhp engine and 700 gpm pump. One of the earliest FT1s had also gone to Birmingham in 1930 as a pump escape and was one of the first Leyland fire engines to run on pneumatic tyres. These gave better overall stability and braking performance, especially when travelling fast en route to fire calls and other emergencies.

FIRST ENCLOSED SALOON BODY

The Merryweather company had a pedigree as one of the principal builders of fire engines going back to manually pumped Victorian days. By 1930 they were truly feeling the competitive pressure and steadily losing ground to the two emerging protagonists, Dennis and Leyland, who between them were increasingly winning the majority of new orders for new fire engines from public and industrial fire brigades. However, Merryweather still managed to poke their two main rivals in the eyes when in 1931 they were commissioned by Edinburgh Fire

Brigade to build the first British all-enclosed limousine type pump. This was based on an Albion chassis. When delivered, the Edinburgh enclosed Merryweather pump signalled a further change towards enclosed fire engine bodywork design, thus providing safer and out of the weather crew accommodation and a more effective use of the available body space for locker stowage.

Yet in spite of all the developments towards enclosed limousine type bodies and inside crew seating, open style Braidwood bodies continued to be specified well into the 1930s by many brigades and built and delivered by Dennis and Leyland, as well as Merryweather and various other small builders. There were even examples, such as the 1936 Dennis Light Four pump escape for Oakham and Uppingham Joint Fire Brigade in Rutland, where despite a cosy enclosed cab for the driver and officer in charge, the poor old crew still had to hang on down each side of the Braidwood body in all weathers!

RIVALRY GROWS

As their order books grew, both Dennis and Leyland kept a continual watch on each other's commercial and marketing activities, together with their respective technical developments. These included features such as dual ignition systems, electric engine heaters and inbuilt battery charging systems to ensure an instant start-up and turnout especially during the winter months.

The early 1930s saw Dennis offering a range of pumping fire engine models including the Dennis Big 4 with its 90 bhp four-cylinder side valve D3 engine, and rear-mounted two-stage turbine pump producing 800 gpm at 70 psi. This was followed by the sister model Big 6 with a 115 bhp six-cylinder engine, and a two-stage pump mounted either at the rear, or amidships if the machine was to carry a 50 ft wheeled escape.

All this competition was good news for fire brigade customers as more and more variants of body style and design became available, but, as the subsequent wartime firefighting challenges were to demonstrate, these did little to bring about a sensible measure of standardisation amongst British fire engines.

PIGS DO FLY

As if to illustrate this, in 1934 Dennis introduced a short wheelbase fire engine based on their new Ace bus chassis. With its very short, snub-nosed bonnet the Ace provided a very manoeuvrable and compact fire engine for both city and rural brigades. Very soon, the Ace was, perhaps somewhat unkindly, nicknamed 'The Flying Pig' because it did indeed have something of an animal face about its front aspect.

BEDFORD ENTERS THE FRAY

Another name which would soon enjoy a long association with British fire engines appeared on the scene in 1933, when the first Bedford fire engine was built for the Princes Risborough Fire Brigade in Buckinghamshire. It was named 'The Prince', after the popular vogue of fire brigades of that time to commemorate local worthies and notables.

Built at the Vauxhall Motors factory at Luton, the first Bedford fire engines were based on a two-ton chassis with a 44 hp six-cylinder engine. These pioneer models were rather basic and pulled trailer pumps as no inboard pumps were fitted. Very soon came a longer wheelbase Bedford model using a 57 hp power unit and with a 350 gpm pump. These second-generation Bedfords could carry a wheeled escape ladder. In late 1933, Luton Fire Brigade took delivery of two of these Mark II Bedford pump escapes, notable for having one of the first examples of transverse inboard seating for the crew behind the driver and officer in charge.

The origins of these first Bedford fire engines lay with the number of Chevrolet trucks built in Britain during the years 1928-1931, several of which were used as fire tenders, one of the first of which was that going to the order of The Liverpool Salvage Corps.

This 1933 Bedford pump is pictured new at time of delivery to Horsham Fire Brigade, Sussex. It has a Braidwood body, midships-mounted 400 gpm pump and 30 ft extension ladder. (Author's collection)

A 1935 Dennis Big 4 pump escape delivered new to Bedford Fire Brigade. (Roger Pennington)

SCAMMELL JOINS IN

During the 1930s other commercial names already well established in the road haulage field made their first foray into the fire engine world. One of these was Scammell. With their manufacturing base at Watford, they had long been a famous and successful manufacturer of lorries and trucks, but as the economic slump of the time intensified, the local brigade presumably felt obliged to order the first of two new pump escapes from their local company. Powered by an 85 hp four-cylinder OHV engine, Watford's first impressive-looking Scammell had a Braidwood body, 400 gpm midships pump, a 40-gallon tank and carried a 55 ft wheeled escape ladder. History subsequently records that after the Watford order, other than for a few fire vehicles built to government order during World War II, it was not until Scammell acquired the Thornycroft airfield crash tender business in the late 1970s that the company once more returned to specialist fire engine manufacture.

SMALL VOLUME BUILDERS

Other small volume fire engine builders of the 1930s included Halley Motors who over the decade delivered 11 Braidwood style pumps to Glasgow Fire Brigade. A number of fire engines also appeared built on Morris Commercial chassis. Some of these had inbuilt pumps (the C type chassis), whilst others destined for rural fire brigade use utilised the two-ton standard Morris Commercial van chassis. This was adapted to accommodate a crew rear compartment and engineered to draw a 350 gpm trailer pump. Several specialist bodybuilders also used various commercial chassis to meet particular fire brigade body specifications. Predominant amongst these were John Morris and Sons of Manchester (mostly using Dennis chassis) and John Kerr & Company also of Manchester (using Albions).

TURNTABLE LADDERS

This was also the period of great advances in turntable ladder design and technology. As far back as 1922, Glasgow Fire Brigade had commissioned an 85 ft model with a Morris chassis, using German-built Magirus wooden ladder sections. This TL took its power from the road engine for all its various evolutions. Neither were Leyland slow to see the growing opportunity to provide more effective high-rise firefighting facilities. In 1924, they staged the first UK appearance of another German-built TL, the Metz, with the first 85 ft version going to Manchester Fire Brigade. Having built several wooden turntable ladders for overseas brigades, including a 93-footer for Shanghai in 1925, Merryweather also got in on the TL action. The London based company built their own TL ladder and mechanism, and in 1932 delivered a 100 ft model, this time to Hong Kong.

Later that same year came a real breakthrough in TL design when the first all-steel Magirus TL appeared in the United Kingdom. Supplied by John Morris and Sons for the London Fire Brigade, this was claimed to be the first all-mechanical TL of its kind in Britain. Within a year, 17 British brigades were using Morris/Magirus TLs, whilst Merryweather's first all-steel TL, an 85 ft version built on an Albion chassis was also built in 1933 to the order of Ilford Fire Brigade.

Meanwhile, Leyland consolidated their contract with Metz and in the same year their first joint all-steel TL went to Coventry Fire Brigade. Leyland marketed steel TLs in various working heights, ranging from 92 ft to 150 ft. In 1935, Hull City Police Fire Brigade took delivery of a six-section 150 ft Leyland/Metz, making it not only the longest TL in use by the British Fire Service, but at the time the tallest fire engine in the world.

This 1939 Leyland FKT1 pump escape of the London Fire Brigade represents a fine example of British fire engine development at the outbreak of World War II. (London Fire Brigade)

This July 1958 photograph depicts a London Fire Brigade crew at work extricating an Armstrong Siddeley that has crashed through the railings and dropped into a basement area in Claverton Street, Pimlico. Since this view taken 50 years ago, non-fire emergencies, or special services as they are termed, have increased nationally to become almost 40 per cent of the fire service's workload. The picture shows one of London Fire Brigade's two 10-ton Dennis breakdown lorries that were used at that time in a variety of emergency operational roles. Up until the late 1970s, vehicle recovery was seen as a regular part of the fire service role, until the road accident focus turned increasingly to casualty extrication and medical intervention skills. The last LFB breakdown lorry was withdrawn in 1977 and is now in preservation. (London Fire Brigade)

CHAPTER FOUR

Prelude To War

When the Luftwaffe bombed several cities and towns during the Spanish Civil War using both incendiaries and high explosives, thousands of civilians were killed amid the huge conflagrations that burned out of control. Soon after, the British government started to wake up to the generally uncoordinated state of fire brigades and the growing aerial fire threat to the United Kingdom and its population.

SOMETHING OF A MOTLEY COLLECTION

By 1935, the United Kingdom was served by no fewer than 1,638 separate and very disparate fire brigades, working under the control and funding of county council, urban district or parish authorities.

At one end of this scale were the professionally manned city brigades such as the London Fire Brigade (LFB) with its 2,500 regular officers and firemen based at 62 fire stations across the capital. London firefighters manned 106 modern front line pumps together with a number of special appliances such as turntable ladders and emergency tenders. By contrast, in rural areas of the country there existed many one pump parish brigades, still likely to be running a single ancient Braidwood-bodied fire engine of World War I vintage with solid tyres, antiquated equipment, and manned by a handful of enthusiastic volunteers. In the 1930s some rural brigades still managed to retain a horse-drawn Shand Mason or Merryweather steam pump.

A LACK OF NATIONAL STANDARDS

Nationally, there was little overall standardised firefighting equipment in operational use. Geographically adjacent brigades often could not reinforce each other at serious fires due to incompatible types of

fire hose. City brigades were beginning to use hose with instantaneous couplings although there was plenty of the old vee-thread screw connection hose around. Nor were there any common fire service rank structures, training or operational command and control procedures.

In 1935, against this very diverse and uncoordinated background, the government set up an inquiry chaired by Lord Riverdale to review the whole structure and efficiency of British fire brigades. The outcome of the Riverdale inquiry was to bring about the 1938 Fire Brigade Act, in which Parliament for the first time placed a statutory duty upon local authorities to provide and maintain an efficient fire brigade.

THE CREATION OF THE AUXILIARY FIRE SERVICE

Before long, the clouds of war in Europe were to have a major impact on the future United Kingdom fire service and its organisation. In 1937, the Home Office required local authorities to submit Air Raid Precautions schemes for their respective areas, and in January 1938, the Air Raid Precautions Act became effective, making a financial provision for the recruitment and training of a new volunteer reserve firefighting force to be known as the Auxiliary Fire Service (AFS).

Unfortunately, despite intense advertising and enrolment campaigns, recruitment into the AFS was disappointing; it took the Munich crisis later on in 1938 to bring forth volunteers in large numbers. Across the London Fire Brigade area, the government's aim was to recruit 28,000 AFS operational reserve firemen, together with 2,000 firewomen for

communications duties. Once recruited, the AFS volunteers undertook 60 hours of basic ladder and pump training and were then posted to satellite AFS substations, mostly located in hastily requisitioned buildings. On recruitment, AFS personnel were asked to sign an undertaking that, in event of war, they would leave their peacetime job and become full-time firefighters.

THE WARTIME FIRE ENGINES

Government aid for the AFS included the funding for additional pumping fire engines and trailer pumps, together with a number of 100 ft turntable ladders and portable water dam units to supplement the peacetime vehicle complement of city and urban fire brigades.

Unfortunately, delivery of the government fire engines to the AFS reserve firefighting force was slow, although it began to gather pace by the autumn of 1939. As a result of these delays, a number of flat bed lorries were temporarily pressed into AFS service up and down the country, capable of carrying portable pumps and serving as general-purpose vehicles to fill the gaps before the new AFS fire engines started to arrive.

Pictured in Bethnal Green Road in London's East End in the summer of 1939, this London AFS Fordson 7V heavy pumping unit has a top-mounted 700 gpm Sulzer pump powered by a Ford engine. The crew are seated in the rear-facing open compartment. Note the 35-foot extension ladder, two hook ladders, 5.5-inch suction hose and the poster trailing Oswald Mosley's 'black shirts'.
(London Fire Brigade)

THE HEAVY UNITS

There were two basic types of AFS firefighting pumps: the utility self-propelled heavy unit and the trailer pump. Heavy units were constructed by a number of coachbuilders using various commercial flatbed chassis. Most had a firefighting pump driven from a separate engine, rather than a power take-off from the road engine. Initially, Austin, Bedford, Fordson and Morris Commercial chassis were all utilised for the heavy units, but with the huge military demand, the Austin K4 and Fordson 7V chassis was eventually adopted by the Home Office as the standard for wartime AFS heavy pumping fire engines.

The 5-ton Austin K4 heavy units had a 3.5-litre six-cylinder petrol engine, four-speed gearbox and hydraulic brakes, whilst some of the first V8-engined Fordson 7Vs on the scene were configured to carry 50 ft wheeled escapes. To accommodate these escape ladders, a number of Fordson 7Vs were fitted with front-mounted pumps. All AFS fire engines were delivered to brigades in battleship grey.

The heavy units were generally fitted with 700 gpm-capacity pumps. Both Austin and Morris Commercial models utilised a Leyland-powered Gwynne pump; the Bedford and Fordson versions used a Ford-engined Sulzer pump, whilst some Fordson-driven Tangye pumps were fitted to Bedford and Fordson heavy units. With no water tank provision, the AFS heavy units were designed primarily to work directly from open water using 5.5-inch suction hose. Firefighting water was delivered through four instantaneous 2.5-inch delivery hose outlets. Most of the heavy units also carried a 35 ft extension ladder whilst the firemen rode in a rear-facing open-backed crew compartment. A number of extra-heavy units with a 1,100 gpm pump were also built, primarily for water relay use. After the war, quite a number of the K4s and 7Vs remained in operational peacetime service in red livery until replaced with more

---

LONDON TAXIS GO TO WAR

When the London AFS started to receive its first batch of 100 new trailer pumps in late 1939, the problem, as elsewhere, was the ready availability of suitable towing vehicles. The London AFS alone was due to receive over 1,700 trailer pumps and the problem in the capital was particularly acute. The short-term solution before the arrival of the new Austin K2 Auxiliary Towing Vehicles was provided when the fire authority, the London County Council, 'hired' over 2,000 London Austin taxis. Strongly constructed and with a tight turning circle, London taxis were ideal for the job. They were able to carry a number of rolled hose lengths and other firefighting equipment in the luggage compartment, and still have room for a crew of five firemen. In many cases, the taxis came with their drivers who became part-time members of the AFS. Most London taxis went to war with the meter still in place!

modern fire engines during the mid 1950s. Today, several Austin K4 and Fordson 7V AFS heavy units survive in preservation.

TRAILER PUMPS A PLENTY

The two-wheeled AFS trailer pumps were designed to be pulled by any suitable towing vehicle and the government ordered these in large quantities from several manufacturers. Various trailer pump types included the lightweight Coventry Climax 220 gpm FSM model and the Beresford Stork 120 gpm version. Both these models could be readily dismounted from their trailers and pushed on their own wheels to the open water source. Heavy output 500 gpm trailer pumps were built in large numbers by makers including Coventry Climax (whose products came to sport the Godiva brand name), Dennis and Scammell.

A SHORTAGE OF TOWING VEHICLES

As the trailer pumps began to be delivered to brigades during 1939, there was an increasing shortage of suitable towing vehicles. Fire chiefs used requisitioning powers to press a wide variety of private cars and light vans into service as towing vehicles, before the Home Office moved quickly to head this off difficulty by ordering a large number of auxiliary towing units (ATVs). These were delivered from early 1940 onwards, and were based upon the Austin K2 2-ton chassis with a square open-backed utility body with bench seats and storage space inside. A 30 ft extension ladder was also carried. In addition to the Austin ATVs, Ford also supplied some 15 cwt utility versions although most of these went into service with the London AFS.

NEW RED LEYLANDS FOR LONDON

Away from the delivery of AFS heavy and trailer pumps, the larger city brigades continued to order new custom-built red fire engines. The London Fire Brigade took delivery of an order of 11 Leyland FKT enclosed dual-purpose pumps to replace older front line open machines. These Leylands were delivered in the spring of 1940 and all went immediately into service at inner London regular fire stations. With an eye to likely war firefighting, the original specification of these Leylands was amended to include a 1,000 gpm pump, and the fitting of a two-inch swivelling monitor. These were the first red LFB fire engines to be so fitted.

UNUSUAL SCAMMELLS

A rather novel wartime utility mini-fire engine was produced by Scammell for use by industrial fire brigades. This was based on an extended Scammell MH6 3 wheeled mechanical horse chassis with a

Although AFS firewomen were recruited for communication, driving and other non-front line duties, their training did include basic hydrant drill. Here in June 1940 several London AFS firewomen get a jet to work in the drill yard of Lambeth HQ. Note the regular LFB Dennis Big 4 pump escape close by. (London Fire Brigade)

rear-mounted transverse 50 gpm pump driven off the road engine and a 350-gallon water tank feeding two hose reels. With a 30 ft extension ladder, these mini Scammells were some of the more unusual fire engines of the World War II period.

MORE TURNTABLE LADDERS

Another problem arose with the declining peacetime availability of new all-steel 100 ft turntable ladders. From the mid-1930s, TL ladder sections and mechanisms for British brigades had predominantly been imported from two German manufacturers, Metz and Magirus. By the late 1930s, supplies of these had naturally dried up, causing the Home Office to turn to Merryweather to make up the shortfall. By 1940, some 20 additional 100 ft Merryweather TLs, mostly mounted on an AEC or Dennis chassis, had been delivered to various large city brigades to reinforce their high-rise firefighting capability. One Merryweather TL feature was that when in use, the ladder operator rode on the rotating turret and from there worked the various foot clutches and levers to extend, elevate and train the ladder sections into the required position. This meant that the operator could see the head of the ladder at all times.

WAR IS DECLARED

When war was declared on 3 September 1939, AFS personnel were immediately called up to man their pumps and trailer pumps located at substations in schools, garages, factories and other requisitioned buildings, many far from suitable for use as fire stations. In the capital,

From the outbreak of war, AFS crews usually had to contend with some pretty unsuitable and cramped accommodation. This group of sheds is Bath Street AFS substation, Shoreditch, in the City of London in August 1940. From left to right the AFS vehicles are: a 1940 Morris heavy unit; a Fordson 35 cwt van with trailer pump; another Morris heavy unit; a Ford towing unit and a Wolseley staff car. (Author's collection)

in addition to the 62 regular LFB stations, London AFS personnel crewed some 360 substations.

However, by late 1939, the expected Blitz had not materialised and the fire service was able to use the precious months into early 1940 to continue the issue of equipment and uniforms, and further consolidate the training of AFS firemen and women. Surprisingly, during the lull of 1939/early 1940, the two branches of the service, regular and AFS, were not readily integrated. Bearing in mind that the AFS crews were drawn from all walks of life and most had never experienced a real fire, this was an incomprehensible decision. Up to the spring of 1940, the auxiliaries were not allowed to attend peacetime fires to gain basic live firefighting experience. The AFS went to plenty of exercises and drills but before long, began to be derided as 'column dodgers'. Even the *Daily Mirror* had a sustained go at the inactivity of the auxiliaries. The morale of the AFS continued to slide to an all-time low until mid-August 1940 when the fire service war started in earnest. During the early stages of the Battle of Britain, many RAF airfields were raided. There were many serious fires to be dealt with, and on 17 August, the first incendiary bombs fell on properties in the Woolwich and Eltham areas of southeast London.

THE FIRST MAJOR BLITZ

However, later that same month, the Luftwaffe turned their full strategic attention to the extensive oil installations of the Thames estuary. On 24 August 1940, a huge fire was started when incendiaries and high explosives fell on the Thameshaven fuel depot. The local Essex firefighting resources, both regular and AFS, were soon stretched to the limit and for the first time under the regional command structure now in place, a 50-pump reinforcement was sent from the LFB. For the first time, this consisted mostly of AFS crews with their heavy units and trailer pumps.

The same night also saw the first Blitz high explosive and incendiary raid on central and east London. This raid also hit the City of London and parts of the dockland and although modest in overall size and duration compared with what was soon to come, it provided a very clear illustration of the sheer number of pumps and manpower that were going to be required. On the night of 24 August the fire burning right along Fore Street in the City required 200 pumps alone, both heavy units and trailer pumps, and the efforts of 1,000 firefighters. Other serious fires of a similar size were burning in the nearby West India Docks but all were finally brought under control by the dawn.

By the morning of 25 August 1940, several thousand London AFS firefighters had received their baptism by fire and tasted the smoke of battle. Sadly, a number were killed and injured during this first major Blitz raid. As the huge fires came under control, little did the firemen know of the far worse, prolonged and unrelenting pyrotechnic hell they would face over the weeks and months that lay ahead. The coming intense Blitz period was not only to challenge London's entire firefighting force, both professional and AFS, but was to concern every fireman in the land as they heard the news from London and anxiously watched the skies over their particular patch.

Burning fuel tanks at Thameshaven, Essex, soon after the first wave of German bombers had struck on 24 August 1940. The firefighting effort is only just getting underway and fire is beginning to spread to other oil tanks as further bombers approach. Note the explosion damage to tanks not yet on fire. (Author's collection)

CHAPTER FIVE

The Blitz And The Coming Of The National Fire Service

By the end of September 1940, the fire service in London and the South East was beginning to understand that it was going to be a long and bloody war. Since the outbreak of war one year earlier, both regular firefighters and the men and women of the Auxiliary Fire Service (AFS) had braced themselves for the worst. Now the firefighters' war had arrived with a terrible fiery vengeance.

LONDON IS THE TARGET

Ever since the end of the Battle of Britain, the Luftwaffe had probed the home defences ever closer to the capital with sporadic high explosive and incendiary raids. On the night of 7 September, the full force of German bombers was turned on London..

This first targeted Blitz raid on the capital and its population only lasted for one and a half hours, but its effect was devastating. Up to that time, it is incredible to relate that four fifths of London's AFS crews had never attended a real fire. Since 1939, AFS activity up and down the country had been largely confined to training, the occasional major exercise, and plenty of cleaning and polishing of their heavy units, trailer pumps and towing vehicles. In London, a few AFS firemen were selected as 'red riders' and allowed to ride the red Dennis and Leyland fire engines of the regular London Fire Brigade (LFB).

FIRE OVER THE DOCKS

These were the lucky chaps, able to get some firefighting experience at peacetime fires over the months of 1940 during the build-up to the Blitz proper. Not so the rest of the AFS, who were literally thrown into the arena as the bombs rained down during the late afternoon

A typical picture of a London Fire Brigade turntable ladder at work during the September 1940 Blitz. The TL is working as a water tower in Queen Victoria Street in the City and looks to be almost at maximum 100 ft height. (Author's collection)

of 7 September. Huge fires were started in the dockland area from East and West Ham, through the Royal Docks, across whole areas of East London, Woolwich Arsenal, and the highly vunerable Surrey Docks, where the warehouses stored one and a half million tons of imported timber.

Within half an hour of the raid starting, West Ham were already asking London Regional Fire Control for 500 pumps. At Surrey Docks, over 200 pumps were committed within an hour of the first pump arriving at the scene. The uncontrolled fire spread rapidly. By 1830 hrs, the fire engine availability boards at London Control looked decidedly empty as reinforcements were called up from the surrounding brigades of the Home Counties. By midnight, over 1,000 separate fire incidents were being dealt with by over 2,200 pumps. The Surrey Docks was soon being officially classed as a conflagration, a half a mile square area of uncontrolled fire.

Fortunately, this raid came when the Thames was at high tide and the fireboats of the London Fire Service were able to get considerable quantities of water ashore to the worst affected areas. By dawn on 8 September, most of the huge fires were coming under control, although a thick fog of pungent smoke hung over much of the fire areas of South and East London and for some hours, fine grey ash fell like snow from the sky to cover fire crews and their fire engines in a ghostly mantle.

After this night when over 450 civilians were killed in their homes and seven firemen died in the streets, the LFB War Diary rather understated the action when it recorded:

"A big enemy raid caused great fires at Surrey Docks, East and West India Docks and the Royal Arsenal, which taxed the whole of the London Fire Service."

57 UNRELENTING DAYS AND NIGHTS

The pattern was thus set for London firefighters for the next 57 unrelenting days and nights as the Luftwaffe returned to bomb and set fire to more of the capital's buildings. For London's fire crews, each daytime was to merge into nights and then weeks of physical danger and arduous effort. By 16 September, London's fire chief, Major Frank Jackson, reported that during the previous week's raids, two LFB officers, 19 firemen and one firewoman had been killed, and 31 LFB regulars, 120 AFS firemen, three firewomen and one youth had been very seriously injured. Sadly, 11 AFS personnel were missing presumed dead. Three LFB fire stations, Whitechapel, Southwark, and Euston had been hit and 18 AFS substations in the central area damaged beyond use.

The demands placed at this time upon the fire engines of both the LFB and its AFS were enormous, particularly the pumping capacity and reliability of the AFS units. In London these were mostly Austin K4 and Fordson 7V heavy units, along with trailer pumps pulled largely

From 1941, the National Fire Service received large numbers of Austin auxiliary towing vehicles (ATVs) primarily for towing trailer pumps. ATVs were built on the 2-ton K2 chassis and powered by a 24 hp six-cylinder petrol engine. Many ATVs survived well after the war years and this 1942 model is pictured still in operational use with the County Borough of Hastings Fire Brigade. It was finally retired in the early 1960s. Note the front-mounted pump, short extension ladder and roof-mounted suction hose. (Maurice Cole/Fire Service National Museum collection)

by requisitioned Austin taxis. Between them these bore most of the brunt of the water relay work. Getting fuel out to the pumps in the street and feeding the weary crews was another priority during the long hours of firefighting, and AFS firewomen volunteers found themselves in the front line action driving petrol carriers loaded with jerry cans and manning the much-needed canteen vans.

But the Blitz was soon to spread beyond London. When exhausted London firefighters finally got a respite from the continuous raiding in November 1940, the Luftwaffe turned their attention to the provinces.

COVENTRY AND THE PROVINCIAL BLITZ

Coventry took a particular pounding from explosives and incendiaries on 14 November. This raid lasted for 11 hours and killed more than 500 civilians. Coventry Fire Brigade was able to contain the fire for about four hours before it became clear that a firestorm was developing, with vast quantities of air being drawn in to feed the raging flames. Coventry city centre, including its historic cathedral, was progressively engulfed by fire. Firefighting reinforcements were urgently summoned from other regions, including as far away as London, but as the first of other West Midlands brigades arrived in Coventry, there was little apparent

London was one of several large cities provided with NFS emergency tenders (ETs) to supplement the brigade's peacetime complement. This Dennis ET is pictured new in NFS livery and was attached to 34 Fire Force, London Region. It carried additional breathing sets, floodlighting from an onboard generator and heavy rescue equipment. (London Fire Brigade)

coordination, firefighting water was scarce and many local pumps had run out of fuel. Worse still, some hose lines had incompatible couplings making water relays a difficult and frustrating exercise.

Several nights later it was Birmingham's turn, before the Luftwaffe turned their attacks to the ports and Southampton suffered several severe raids during the last week of November 1940. By then, the first expressions of the need for a unified national firefighting force were being made, both from within the fire service and in government. There were now plenty of examples of incompatible equipment hindering operations, in addition to the major problem of fireground command. Not unnaturally, a local chief fire officer did not take too kindly to a senior LFB officer arriving in the provinces with his 50-pump convoy expecting to take overall command of the fire situation.

THE BIRTH OF THE NATIONAL FIRE SERVICE

But firefighters in the provincial cities continued to tackle huge fires as best they could under these trying circumstances. Apart from individual raids on industrial cities and ports, London took a regular battering through to April 1941, by which time the need for the creation of a nationalised fire service was obvious. For some weeks, the Home Secretary, Herbert Morrison, had been lobbied by senior fire service figures and after consultations with local government officials, a four-hour meeting at Westminster on the night of 18 April 1941 gave birth to the National Fire Service (NFS).

The Fire Service (Emergency Provisions) Bill 1941 was introduced into the Commons on 13 May 1941 and received royal assent nine days later. The NFS actually came into being on 18 August 1941. Its broad structure amalgamated all 1,638 existing public fire brigades and their regular and AFS personnel, fire engines and equipment into 12 regions, each being subdivided into fire force areas. Funded by considerable government finance, immediate steps were introduced to try to standardise hose and pump fittings, rank structures and uniforms, and provide better communications. New national training regimes were introduced with standard training manuals and promotion study material being widely available.

MORE FIRE ENGINES FOR THE NFS

Attention was also turned within the new NFS towards the central provision of more suitable purpose-built fire engines to replace many hastily and unsuitable requisitioned vehicles pressed into service in some places, both as pumps and towing vehicles. In late 1941, the first of hundreds of NFS auxiliary towing vehicles, known as ATVs, were issued to fire force areas. These were based upon the Austin K2 2-ton chassis powered by a 24 hp six-cylinder petrol engine. Many of these robust and reliable Austin ATVs continued to serve operationally in various guises after the war in county borough and county brigades until final retirement in the late 1960s.

Following the severe Blitz raids of 1940-41, the need for additional turntable ladders was also clearly identified and in 1942, the NFS received 55 new four-section 100ft Merryweather TLs destined for operations in cities and large towns across the United Kingdom. 29 of these TLs were built on the Leyland TD7 half cab bus chassis, whilst the remaining 26 utilised the forward control Leyland TSC18 Beaver chassis. All these TLs had inboard mounted 500 gpm pumps to provide an independent water supply for the TL's monitor. In addition to these Leylands, Dennis teamed up with Merryweather between 1941 and 1943 to build 43 100 ft TLs for NFS regions across the country.

To supplement this increase in city high-rise firefighting capacity, in 1943 the NFS took delivery of the first of 50 hand-operated three-section 60 ft Merryweather TLs based upon the Austin K4 chassis. Like the ATVs, a number of these 100 ft and 60 ft TLs survived in operational use well into post-war years.

Other NFS issue fire engines included Fordson and Dodge mounted mobile dam Units. These provided portable dams and pumps to facilitate large-scale water relays upon which the success of so much wartime firefighting depended.

V1 AND V2 TERROR WEAPONS

In addition to a significant increase and improvement in the fire engine complement of the NFS came more firefighters. By 1942, the establishment of the London NFS Region alone was some 42,000 firemen and women. However, the NFS was never really tested by fire.

CITY UNDER ATTACK

On the night of 29 December 1940, the Luftwaffe concentrated a heavy attack on the square mile of the City of London dropping over 100,000 incendiaries in two hours. The area between St Pauls and the Barbican district was badly affected; Whitecross Street in particular was a veritable death trap. 30 pumps and their crews were at work in this street when the conflagration began to spread from both ends. Eventually the crews had no alternative but to abandon their fire engines and escape down onto the London Transport Metropolitan Underground line to safety. This aerial view taken the morning after the devastating City of London incendiary raid of 29 December 1940 shows part of Whitecross Street and some of the remains of the many abandoned LFB Leyland and Dennis pump escapes and pumps and AFS Fordson heavy units completely burnt out there. *(London Fire Brigade)*

Although there were sporadic explosive and incendiary raids on London and elsewhere in 1942-43, it was the coming of the V1 flying bombs in June 1944 and the V2 rockets in September 1944 in London and the South East that focused the fire service's attention on techniques for the rescue of persons trapped under collapsed buildings. The V1s and V2s were truly explosive weapons and although the V1 gave audible warning of its approach through its ram jet motor, the more lethal V2 with one tonne of explosive literally fell out of the sky. Up to the end of hostilities in 1945, no fewer than 2,381 V1 flying bombs and 511 V1 rockets had fallen on the London NFS region. 900 of these incidents involved fire as well as rescue and recovery from collapsed buildings.

DENATIONALISATION

When hostilities finally ended in 1945, the NFS was a well organised, prepared and equipped firefighting force. However, during the necessary haste to nationalise the fire service back in 1941, the Home Secretary undertook to return it to local authority control as soon as practicable after the war. Thus on 1 April 1948, a dramatic firefighting era ended when the fire service was transferred from national control back to that of county councils and county boroughs. Compared to the 1,638 individual pre-war brigades, 147 mostly enlarged fire brigades emerged from the NFS years.

The early 1950s were to see a quiet revolution in fire engine design and construction as the first national type specifications appeared. New technology and materials heralded better fire engine performance for fire brigades, large and small, up and down the land.

CHAPTER SIX

The Road To Recovery

In the immediate post-World War II period, fire chiefs strove to acquire the emerging new generation of modern pumping fire engines. In many fire brigades, both public and industrial, new pumps were badly needed to replace many unsuitable and worn-out fire vehicles hurriedly commissioned during the run-up to war in 1939.

When the personnel and infrastructure of the National Fire Service (NFS) was duly returned to local authority control on 1 April 1948, with 147 newly formed public fire brigades at city, county and county borough level, there was much for the men and women of the fire service to contemplate about their future.

Whilst the coming of the NFS in 1941 had undoubtedly brought about considerable centralised improvements in equipment, uniforms, training, rank structures and communications, by the end of hostilities the national fire engine fleet remained much as it had been at the outbreak of war. Although the government had supplied considerable numbers of very basic utility heavy units and trailer pumps, together with a number of mobile dam units and turntable ladders to supplement the 1939 fleets of British fire brigades, 10 years later there were still plenty of examples of outdated and ineffective hybrid fire engines in operational use in the front line at many fire stations up and down the land.

THE FIRST NATIONAL SPECIFICATIONS

However, in 1948 as the fire service was being returned to local authority control, the Home Office issued the first set of national fire engine design standards, known as the JCDD fire engine specifications (after the Joint Committee for Design and Development).

These were formulated to produce some standard operational design features found desirable during the rigours of the Blitz firefighting years. 50 years and more on, these post-war standards have served the fire service well right up to the recent arrival of European harmonised standards.

First came water tender specifications (JCDD 3), whose detail had evolved from the basic design of mobile dam units in use throughout the latter years of the war. The JCDD A and B Type water tender specifications set out the technical details for compact fire engines that were to shape the post-war standard maid-of-all-work pumping fire engines for many years to come.

The Type A water tender embraced those that had no inboard fitted pump and usually towed a trailer pump, whilst the Type Bs had an inboard pump, preferably rear mounted, and a 500 gpm capacity at 100 psi output. B Type water tenders were required to provide a cab for a crew of five firemen, and to carry a minimum of 400 gallons of water, an extension ladder, and a light portable pump. B Type variations in JCDD3/1 included the water tender ladder (WrL) that carried a 45 ft alloy extension ladder, and the water tender escape (WrE) with a 50 ft wooden wheeled escape ladder.

In addition to JCDD 3, other post-war Home Office specifications were issued, including JCDD 18 which detailed a classification of pump (P) and pump ladder (PL) for urban areas, whilst JCDD 4 covered dual purpose (DP) appliances. These were pumps that could be easily adapted to carry either a wheeled escape or an extension ladder. In practice, most DPs served in brigades in the cities and other metropolitan areas.

A fine line-up of Birmingham fire engines outside Central Fire Station in Corporation Street during the last days of the National Fire Service, circa 1947. From left to right: an Austin staff car; a 1939 Leyland SKFT rescue tender EDJ 877; a 1935 Leyland Metz 104 ft turntable ladder BOF 389; 1934 Leyland New World pumps BOF 386 and DOK 831 and a 1939 SKFT pump escape EDJ 878. (Author's collection)

A DENNIS REAWAKENING

Not surprisingly, fire engine manufacturers were clearly anxious to get back into the post-war fire engine market. As early as the latter part of 1945, Dennis Brothers quickly dusted off a revamped version of their successful pre-war Light 4 model fitted with a 500 gpm pump, and two years later, the first Dennis model F1 rolled off the production line at Guildford, although this was still an open-bodied fire engine.

AEC JOINS THE FRAY

Merryweather followed in 1948 with a completely new pumping fire engine that utilised a shortened version of the AEC Regent Mk III chassis. This was initially powered by a six-cylinder petrol engine, had a 500-gallon water tank and a 1,000 gpm midships mounted pump. Later Merryweather AEC Regent pumps used the AEC 9.6-litre diesel engine and although not being renowned for their fast response speeds, the AECs nevertheless endeared themselves to fire service drivers with their good manners and steady and reliable performance, both on the road and whilst pumping.

DENNIS CLASSICS

Two years later, Dennis launched their forward control F7, a truly stylish looking fire engine with a 162-inch wheelbase chassis that came either with a rear or midships mounted pump and dual hose reel drums fed from a 100-gallon tank. In 1950, the Dennis F7 was superseded by the F12 that sported a 12-inch shorter wheelbase and some cosmetic bodywork improvements whilst still retaining the sweeping lines of the already popular F7.

No doubt one reason for the popularity of these new Dennis models was that they were pretty quick out on the road. Their Rolls Royce straight eight-cylinder B80 Mark X 5.7-litre 195 bhp power units could attain a speed of 60 mph within 45 seconds. For a fully equipped pump, this was a performance virtually unheard off in those days. The Dennis F12 quickly captured a large section of the British fire brigade pumping market. For instance, by 1954 Middlesex Fire Brigade was using the Dennis F7 and F12 almost exclusively as its standard pumping fire engine. Some 336 F12s were built at Dennis's Guildford factory between 1950 and 1959 and it is pleasing to see a number of these classic fire engines in active preservation.

In 1950, Dennis also boldly launched what was to be another hugely successful new product: the limousine-bodied F8. Powered by a Rolls Royce B60 six-cylinder petrol engine, the F8 was probably the first truly compact rural fire engine, being only 6 ft 6 in wide against the conventional 7 ft 6 in. Up to 1950 Dennis had always delivered complete

ALLOY REPLACES WOOD

The Leyland Comet water tenders of the early 1950s were notable in that they were some of the first fire engines to carry the new aluminium 50 ft extension ladders manufactured by the Merryweather company. These new alloy ladders were a novel departure from the traditional 50 ft wooden wheeled escapes beloved of many city and county borough fire brigades and were the precursor of today's 13.5-metre alloy ladders. However, in the 1950s, despite their specially lowered ladder mounting on the Leyland Comets and other pumps, the solid construction and overall weight of the new Merryweather ladders made them somewhat unwieldy to slip off the fire engine and get to work. At this time Merryweather also produced a steel version of the traditional 50 ft wheeled escape and although this was a much lighter version than its wooden predecessors, it too never really took off in great numbers. Perhaps this said something about the conservative nature of British fire brigades at that time.

fire engines, but in that year the company broke new ground when they began to supply the F8 chassis to specialist bodybuilders such as Alfred Miles of Cheltenham. Dennis ultimately acquired the fire appliance bodywork section of Alfred Miles in 1962. The F8 went on to become another strong seller for Dennis with a total of 245 going into service with British fire brigades between 1952 and 1960.

OTHER MAKES JOIN IN

As the demand for replacement fire engines continued to grow, a number of fire authorities who were still forced to keep a careful eye on their restricted budgets began to commission water tenders based upon suitable commercial chassis such as Albion, Dodge and Commer. The Commer QX model with its underfloor six-cylinder 109 bhp petrol engine was the choice of several county brigades. A number of these Commers were bodied either by Carmichael of Worcester or Hampshire Car Bodies (HCB) of Southampton, two firms who had taken on urgent post-war fire engine bodybuilding work as soon as post-NFS contract work was commercially available, supported by some central governmental finance.

The Bedford badge was also being seen increasingly in fire brigade fleets and by the early 1950s Bedfords, usually built on the J and the later S chassis, were in widespread use as pumps, especially in rural brigades. Alfred Miles built a number of Bedford dual-purpose pumps using the S type chassis, and these were able to carry a 50 ft wheeled escape or run as a water tender with an extension ladder. The S type Bedfords had a 156-inch wheelbase and were powered by a six-cylinder 4.9-litre petrol engine.

The bodywork designed by the Alfred Miles company utilised a folding double door on either side of the cab. It was also around this time that the Miles company began to offer fire vehicles with an option of either wooden framed bodywork or an all-aluminium frame with similar metal panelling. Several brigades soon changed over to metal bodies, which amongst other things were claimed to be lighter, provide greater resistance to rot and were easier to repair or replace in event of an accident.

BIRMINGHAM BEDFORDS

One other notable post-war use of Bedfords was in Birmingham Fire and Ambulance Service. In late 1951 an order for 27 dual-purpose pumps was placed with local bodybuilders Wilsdon & Co of Solihull. These pumps were to replace a number of the city's early 1930s Leyland open fire engines. The new pumps were built on a specially shortened Bedford 126-inch SB series chassis, more normally used for passenger vehicles, and with their integral six-man cab, these Birmingham Bedfords looked every bit a fine and purposeful fire engine. With the standard Bedford 4.9-litre six-cylinder OHV petrol engine, and a rear-mounted 500 gpm pump, these pumps gave valiant operational service to Birmingham over the next two decades.

This 1939 Dodge entered wartime service as a mobile dam unit and was one of several rebuilt after the war by Hampshire Car Bodies when it then went as a water tender to serve with the Isle of Wight Fire Brigade until retirement. This historic fire engine is now in the collection of the Fire Services National Museum Trust, whose intention is to restore the Dodge to its original wartime condition. (Chris Jackson)

LEYLAND'S FINAL FLING

Along with Dennis Bothers, Leyland had enjoyed a very significant chunk of the pre-war fire engine marketplace. However, the company directed most of its post-war attention towards its commercial vehicle customers, somewhat to the detriment of those brigades who had been happy customers for Leyland pumps and turntable ladders throughout the 1930s. Nevertheless, the Leyland badge did make a token appearance again in 1951 when several brigades specified the post-war Comet chassis for new water tender contracts, notably in Kent and Surrey Brigades. With its normal control cab body and 5.6-litre six-cylinder diesel engine, it was unfortunate that the Comet never gained the popularity levels enjoyed by of some of Leyland's fire service competitors, and by the mid 1950s, the company turned its attention completely away from fire engines.

THE FIRST LAND ROVERS

The Series I Land Rover had first appeared on the commercial scene in 1948 and was soon interesting a number of rural fire brigades in the United Kingdom who had quickly identified the off-road capability potential of the new 4 x 4 for firefighting operations in country areas. The very first commercial Land Rovers were built with an 80-inch

A truly classic post-war fire engine. This shining 1949 Rolls Royce-engined Dennis F7 dual-purpose pump of the London Fire Brigade is pictured when new and running as a pump escape attached to LFB Station 61, Albert Embankment, Lambeth. (London Fire Brigade)

wheelbase with a 1600 cc petrol engine. The basic model was devoid
of features that were later to become standard items of Land Rover
equipment and interestingly, essential items such as a power take-off
and winch were shown by Land Rover as optional extras.

By the early 1950s, the Series I Land Rover started to appear in rural
fire brigade fleets for use both as four-wheel drive light pumps and
also to meet the growing need for an all-terrain general purpose fire
and rescue vehicle. Amongst the first fire brigades to introduce Land
Rovers into operational service were Eastbourne County Borough, the
City of Bristol, and Merionethshire County. The equipment inventory
of these early Land Rovers included a short extension ladder, a few
lengths of 2.5-inch hose and a searchlight.

Some of the first Series I Land Rover light firefighting pumps were
ordered with a soft-top configuration. However, it was not long before
several of the bodybuilding companies more used to building full-sized
water tenders started to fit out the new lightweight fire engines. Before
long, Land Rovers began to emerge with an inboard light fire pump
driven off a power take-off with initial firefighting water fed from
a small water tank to a hose reel. A popular alternative to an inbuilt
pump was the demountable Coventry Climax portable pump with its
four-cylinder 350 gpm portable pump, then new on the market. These
portable pumps could be carried by the crew to the actual firefighting
water source such as a lake, river or stream and provided a welcome
flexibility for rural firefighting operations in which Land Rovers were
to become a permanent post-war feature.

CHAPTER SEVEN

The Phoenix Arises:
The Auxiliary Fire Service
Returns

As the 147 post-war public fire brigades moved forward into the early 1950s, fire authorities strived to find sufficient funding to replace hundreds of old and unsuitable fire engines and many items of equipment that had been in front line use throughout the National Fire Service (NFS) years.

DENNIS GET INTO GEAR

Up to the outbreak of World War II, the two principal and long-established fire engine builders of Dennis Brothers and Leyland had between them shared much of the regular new fire service vehicle business. After the war, Dennis had quickly resumed building complete fire vehicles, although by 1953 with Leyland continuing to concentrating its effort on the road haulage, bus and coach market, the Guildford concern's main threat was from various bodybuilders increasingly providing basic fire engines using commercial chassis such as those of Commer and Bedford.

Apart from local authority fire brigade customers, there also were numerous industrial works firefighting units and growing airport fire and rescue services who all provided a steadily developing marketplace for British fire engine manufacturers.

COLD WAR POLITICS

Another factor of a political nature that provided a considerable boost for fire engine builders was the growing post-war hostility between the West and the Soviet Union. This was to have a considerable effect on fire brigades, for in 1948 the government began moves to reconstitute the Auxiliary Fire Service (AFS) as part of the country's civil defence preparedness in event of a nuclear conflict. It was envisaged that the role of the AFS would be to support the regular fire service and provide large quantities of water by relay from areas unaffected by the effects of conflict.

THE AFS RETURNS

By late 1949, quite a few men and women rejoined the AFS after having not long been stood down when the NFS was disbanded and the fire service returned to local authority control. At first, the post-war reconstituted AFS were re-allocated many of the oldest and most worn-out wartime heavy pumps and trailer pumps hastily cobbled together back in 1939. Although the Home Office had identified that the 'new' AFS would need some more modern fire engines, it was not until 1952 that tenders were finally invited for a large number of government funded pumping appliances and support vehicles. After some more bureaucratic delays, the Home Office eventually placed orders for several thousand AFS self-propelled pumps and the first special AFS appliances.

THE GREEN GODDESS IS BORN

All the AFS fire engines were delivered in a dark green livery, and although the Bedford pumps were officially termed self-propelled

Up to 1954 Dennis Brothers had always produced complete fire engines for their many customers. However, in that year Dennis entered into an agreement to supply the F8 chassis to Alfred Miles Ltd of Cheltenham who built a number of F8 compact pumps for rural brigades using the Miles standard body, which was only 78 inches wide. This preserved Dennis/ Alfred Miles F8 shows off its compact lines well. (Keith Wardell collection)

By the early 1950s, many brigades were expanding their non-fire rescue vehicle provision. LOY 999 was a 1953 Bedford SB A emergency tender of Croydon Fire Brigade and carried additional breathing apparatus, a range of powered lifting and cutting gear, floodlighting and chemical suits.
(Keith Wardell collection)

pumps, they soon became better known as Green Goddesses. Before long all of the 147 British fire brigades started to receive an issue of Green Goddesses and several support vehicles for their AFS personnel to train upon. At the time, who would have thought that these green Bedfords would come to have such a lasting place in fire service history some 50 years after their introduction?

The first Green Goddesses were based on the Bedford S type 4 x 2 chassis although once production runs got going, large numbers were built on the R type 4 x 4 version. With such a large government order, the Home Office spread the work for the Green Goddesses around 10 different bodybuilders. Surprisingly, most of these Bedfords were bodied by bus and coachbuilders with none of the traditional fire engine bodybuilders being involved. Amongst the bodybuilders of Green Goddesses were Harrington, Park Royal, Plaxton, Weymann and Willowbrook. Very few of these Bedfords carried a maker's plate and it was difficult to tell the precise origin of a particular AFS pump.

GREEN GODDESS POWER

The Bedford Green Goddesses were powered by a six-cylinder 110 bhp petrol engine. Pumping power was provided by a Sigmund FN4 gunmetal 900 gpm rear-mounted coupling for water relay work using either hose or steel piping. The pump assembly also had a foam inductor connection.

Each Green Goddess provided enclosed crew cab accommodation for six firemen with one folding door on each side of the cab. Various-sized hinged equipment lockers were provided on both sides of the body. The 4 x 2 Bedfords had a 300-gallon water tank (400 gallons on the 4 x 4s), feeding two hose reels. A Coventry Climax FWP light portable pump was also carried inboard, locked on a sliding tray to facilitate removal. Other equipment included 1,600 ft of 2.5-inch rolled delivery hose, various hose fittings and a 35 ft alloy extension ladder.

AFS SUPPORT VEHICLES

In addition to the AFS Bedford pumps, the Home Office also commissioned some 250 vehicles on Bedford and the Commer Q4 chassis configured in a variety of support roles in order to make the AFS truly able to operate as mobile self-contained units. These support vehicles included pipe carriers, hose layers, control units, canteen vans and an unusual vehicle officially termed the transportable water unit or 'Bikini'.

BIKINI UNITS

Each of these Bikinis carried three inflatable rafts and each raft carried a crew of two and three portable 300 gpm pumps to act as floating base pumps for major water relays. The rafts were offloaded by a crane arrangement fitted to the rear of the vehicle. The rafts were themselves powered by the jet reaction from one of the three onboard portable pumps and each Bikini raft unit was therefore capable of pumping 12 tons (2,700 gallons) of water per minute into a relay – quite a formidable performance.

Additional to the AFS Bedford pumps and various Commer special units came some Land Rover and Austin Gypsy 4 x 4 staff vehicles together with a number of Matchless and BSA motorcycles for despatch rider and general communication and convoy duties.

The whole concept of the Cold War AFS was to provide a completely self-contained mobile firefighting column able to tackle the perceived conflagrations of a post-attack nuclear scenario. Part of the concept of the AFS Cold War role was to have the capacity to pump water over considerable distances to its place of need, not just for firefighting. It is clear that in event of war, one of the additional roles of the AFS crews and their green vehicles would have been the widespread provision of drinking water through their long-distance pumping capacity.

THE COLD WAR THAWS

Fortunately for mankind, the operational abilities of the AFS were never to be tested during the Cold War period and, with an increasing thaw in East/West relationships, the AFS was finally disbanded in 1968. A large number of Green Goddesses were, however, placed into storage by the government and progressively upgraded over the years. Military fire crews have used Green Goddesses at intervals over the past three decades during fire service industrial disputes.

A number of Bedford Green Goddesses were also purchased by fire authorities for use as reserve pumps. Once these were acquired they were painted in brigade red livery. Many of these AFS pumps had little mileage on the clock and in rural county brigades these 4 x 4 Bedfords proved to be reliable high-capacity fire tenders, if somewhat technically dated. A number of Green Goddesses remain in preservation, including at least one example of a complete working Commer Q4 Bikini Unit.

TURNTABLE LADDER DEVELOPMENTS

Whilst all this government Cold War activity to re-equip the AFS was going on, 'red' fire engine development continued to gather pace. Merryweather had regained their commercial momentum by 1950. Two years earlier the company had launched its new pump based upon the AEC Regent III chassis and in late 1949 Merryweather delivered the first of ten 100 ft turntable ladders. These were configured for normal control on the AEC Regal coach chassis with a 9.5-litre Meadows petrol engine. The first was delivered to Surrey Fire Brigade and over the next two years a second Merryweather AEC Regal TL went to Surrey, with others going to Lancashire (two), Central Area Scotland, Lanarkshire, Kingston-upon-Hull, Birmingham, Glamorgan and Somerset. At this time, South Eastern Area of Scotland Brigade also took delivery of a Merryweather 100 ft TL built on a diesel-powered forward control AEC Regent chassis.

However, the four ladder sections of all these new Merryweather TLs still used mechanical power for extension, elevation and rotation to a design almost identical to that of the company's pre-war TLs, some of which were still in service. In fact, when the ladder sections and mechanisms were still in sound condition, a number of brigades took the economic option to re-chassis their pre-war TLs and concentrate their funding on the upgrading of their pumping fleets.

NEW MERRYWEATHERS

In 1954 Merryweather also launched its new Marquis light pumping fire engine. This used the AEC/Maudslay chassis but the Mk I version was unsuccessful, winning only six orders. Merryweather licked its wounds and for a while concentrated upon TL production before producing a more successful Mk II and the later III Marquis versions several years later, both using the AEC Mercury chassis.

Meanwhile, Dennis Brothers continued to turn out large numbers of their very successful F12 and F8 pumps to the order of city and urban brigades up and down the country but were not slow in moving their fire engine product range forward. In 1955, having listened to chief officers in several large city brigades who had requested a diesel-powered pumping appliance, Dennis launched their F101. These fine-looking Dennis models had a 12.2-litre Rolls Royce diesel producing 170 bhp with an air-over hydraulic braking system.

First introduced over 50 years ago, AFS Bedford Green Goddesses have been brought into front line use on various occasions. One such time was the period of severe and prolonged wet weather experienced across the South East in January 1994. Here two Bedford R type 4 x 4 Green Goddesses are in action on the Hampshire/West Sussex border, pumping floodwater along a relay towards the sea. Note the use of the rear offside 6-inch full bore connection. (Hampshire Fire & Rescue Service)

Two preserved examples of AFS support vehicles of the 1950s. On the left is a Bedford 4 x 4 Mobile Control Unit with a Commer Q4 Transportable Water Unit (Bikini) on the right. (Author's collection)

A FIRST FOR DENNIS

The F101 made British vehicle history for Dennis, as it became the first company to utilise a Rolls Royce diesel for automotive use. Between 1955 and 1960 London Fire Brigade took delivery of 38 F101s all of which went into service as dual-purpose appliances. Over a similar period, Liverpool became another F101 brigade whilst Nottinghamshire received 14 F102s (the water tender version).

LAUNCH OF THE GAMECOCK

At the 1952 Commercial Motor Show, Karrier Motors had launched the Gamecock water tender. This was the result of collaboration with bodybuilders Carmichael of Worcester and led to a compact fire engine designed for both city and rural county fire brigades. Built to a four-ton payload on 9 ft 7 in wheelbase (later extended to 11 ft 9 in), the Gamecock carried 400 gallons of water and was powered by a Commer underfloor 4.7-litre six-cylinder petrol engine. By 1956, the Gamecock was in widespread use in British brigades with over 100 eventually entering service, not just as pumps but as a variety of special appliances.

DENNIS GO FOR AN AUTOMATIC

In 1956 Dennis launched the F24, which with its four-speed automatic transmission claimed another first for the company. The F24 was powered by the B60 Rolls Royce six-cylinder petrol engine and brigades were able to choose a range of configurations, either dual-purpose or water tender with a choice of pumping units up to 1,000 gpm. For those brigades still wary of automatics (and there were still a few!), Dennis offered the F25 version with a five-speed manual gearbox.

METAL v WOOD BODYWORK

The 1950s were also the time of the great debate on the merits or otherwise of metal versus wood bodywork on fire engines. The Alfred Miles company were one of the foremost exponents of metal body structures and they vigorously promoted the strength and robust nature of the company's new metal construction methods. The first examples of this new style of fire engine bodywork certainly caused a stir. Roller shutters began to be left in an unpainted bright alloy finish and aluminium exteriors went into operational service on numerous Bedford and Commer water tenders in many shire county brigades. In 1953 Kent Fire Brigade claimed that they were able to save £30 per appliance when using embossed aluminium panels instead of paintwork on their new Commer water tenders supplied by Hampshire Car Bodies!

NEW AVIATION CRASH TENDERS

Another area of fire engine development of the 1950s was that of aviation firefighting and rescue. After the war, airfields, like their public fire brigade counterparts, had to make do with well-used vehicles although by the 1950s a new generation of airfield fire engines was beginning to appear. In 1951, the Royal Air Force took delivery of its first post-war crash tender, a Thornycroft Nubian TF 4 x 4 chassis by Sun Engineering with bodywork by the James Whitson company. Powered by a Rolls Royce eight-cylinder B80 petrol engine, some 80 of these crash tenders eventually went into service with the RAF. The Thornycrofts carried 400 gallons of water and 60 gallons of foam and were capable of delivering 2,500 gpm of finished foam.

In 1955, the Pyrene company built a modified version for the RAF using the Thornycroft Mk 5A chassis whilst one year later the company chose an Alvis Salamander 6 x 6 chassis for the first time to meet a government military crash tender order. These unusual specialist fire engines had a light alloy integral body together with a roof-mounted foam monitor. Powered by a Rolls Royce B81 six-cylinder petrol engine developing 240 bhp, over 60 of these crash tenders were built with most remaining in UK operational service until the late 1970s.

Similarly, the 1950s saw the larger of British civil airports beginning to take delivery of new fire and rescue tenders. These were mostly built by Sun Engineering on Thornycroft Nubian 6 x 6 chassis and came in three main configurations: a foam tender, a foam/CO_2 tender, or a water tender. The largest foam output of these could produce 7,500 gpm of finished product in order to keep pace with the increasing size of civil aircraft and the general growth of aviation traffic and airport aircraft movements.

DRAMA AT SMITHFIELD

Smithfield Meat Market, London at dawn on 23 January 1958. This dramatic scene shows thick toxic smoke still pouring from a major basement fire that has been burning all night long. 30 pumps and special appliances and 200 firemen from all over central London attended the incident that was not under control until late into the afternoon. Operations at the Smithfield fire required a very large effort by many crews rigged in breathing apparatus. Early on during the fire, the burning cork-lined insulation and extensive labyrinthine basement passageways under the market halls made it a firefighter's nightmare. Two London firemen lost their lives when their oxygen supplies ran out.

The scene shows some interesting examples of the London Fire Brigade fleet of that time including AEC Merryweather Regent pumps, a Dennis F12 and the newer F101 pumps, and at least one pre-war Leyland pump in the right hand foreground. Also visible in the left foreground are several London Fire Brigade staff cars, and (left centre) a City of London Police control unit with a London County Council Daimler ambulance behind. Further beyond is the LFB Control Unit, whilst a maze of charged hose lines can be seen near one of the basement entry points.

Lessons learnt in the use of breathing apparatus at the Smithfield fire brought about national improvements in various safety features fitted to firefighting breathing sets. *(London Fire Brigade)*

CHAPTER EIGHT

Innovation: Large And Small

By 1960, fire brigades had an unprecedented width of choice of chassis and although the Dennis Brothers factory at Guildford continued to dominate the marketplace in the public and industrial fire brigade sector, the Bedford marque was beginning to become a major rival, particularly for the supply of chassis for compact water tenders for shire county brigades.

BEDFORD BUILD THEIR NUMBERS

Building on their very large fire service presence with hundreds of Green Goddesses built for the reconstituted Auxiliary Fire Service during the early 1950s, Bedford introduced their TJ chassis in 1958. Both these chassis were offered in two options; the J4 (5-ton) and the J5 with its 6-ton rating. These chassis were delivered ex-factory in normal control configuration, but with Bedford's approval, fire engine bodybuilders HCB specialised in converting both types to forward control for their customers. Both the J4 and J5 were immediately popular with a number of county brigades and many of the able Bedfords saw operational service well into the late 1970s. A number of these models incorporated all-metal construction in their bodywork.

Bedford went on to consolidate their share of the fire engine market when in 1960 their first TK chassis appeared. This model also quickly found customers amongst British fire brigades. The first series TKs were fitted with the Bedford 300 series petrol engine and it was not until 1974 that a more powerful diesel engine option became available. By the mid-1960s, Bedford TKs could be seen in service right across the country, both in urban and rural brigades. Many served as pumps but the Bedford TKEL chassis was also used for a growing number of specialist vehicles such as emergency tenders, foam tenders and control units. The heavier TKEL chassis also began to appear as the base for some of the newer post-war turntable ladders with ladder sections built both by Merryweather and Magirus. Coincidentally, in 1963 one of the first of these new Bedford TLs on a TKGL chassis with 100 ft Merryweather ladders went to Bedfordshire Fire Brigade's station in Bedford!

UP IN THE AIR

In 1963 came a particular milestone in the development of high rise firefighting and rescue vehicles when Monmouthshire became the first British fire authority to order a hydraulic platform (HP). This was a 65 ft twin boom Simon SS65 mounted on a Commer VAC chassis with bodywork by Buttons. Passing into the ownership of Gwent Fire Brigade in 1974, this historic fire engine was finally retired in 1980 by which time HPs were well established as versatile and effective aerial firefighting vehicles.

This 1973 Bedford/HCB Angus pump of the City of Coventry shows off its bright yellow livery sported by the brigade's fire engines in an attempt to improve general conspicuity and safety at operational incidents. At the time of the photograph this pump was attached to Canley Fire Station.
(Jerry Hepworth)

The use of hydraulic power for high rise firefighting vehicles was, however, not new. As far back as 1924, Merryweather had constructed a hydraulically powered turntable ladder for Rangoon Fire Brigade. Despite this considerable achievement for that time, it was not until 1957 that the company delivered its first British hydraulic TL when York Fire Brigade received a new 100 ft model based on an AEC Mercury chassis. This was the first of over 100 Merryweather/AEC Mercury TLs to be delivered to British brigades from 1957 through to the early 1990s.

THE RETURN OF LEYLAND

Another interesting landmark in fire engine history was the brief re-emergence in 1959 of the once-powerful Leyland marque. Back in 1950, the company had made a limited and unsuccessful commercial return to the British fire engine market with the Comet chassis. Despite this setback and following some collaboration with Manchester Fire

YELLOW PERILS

The colour of fire engines became a matter of some heated debate amongst British firemen in 1965. This followed the publication of a report by Albert Leese, the Chief Officer of the City of Coventry Fire Brigade, describing various tests carried out with different colours and colour combinations in daylight, night-time and in varying street lighting conditions. CFO Leese decided that fire engines would be more conspicuous and safer if painted bright yellow rather than the traditional red, particularly when at the scene of the increasing number of road crashes attended by fire crews. ICI Paints produced a 'special fire engine yellow' and needless to say, Coventry promptly repainted all its fire engines.

There then followed a period during which several other brigades, notably West Sussex, and Newport, Monmouthshire (subsequently Gwent) adopted yellow for a number of their fleets. Not all brigades were convinced of the efficacy of yellow liveries, although several who supported some sort of colour change went one better than yellow, with both the West Riding of Yorkshire and Bedfordshire Fire Service repainting some fire engines in their fleets in a pure white livery. However, the majority of senior officers in the service were not convinced, preferring to rely on improved warning lights on their existing red machines together with the widespread issue of reflective orange jerkins to personnel to raise safety levels at operational incidents, especially road traffic accidents on the new motorways.

Despite this, most of the yellow and white fire engines retained their striking finishes well beyond the 1974 reorganisation that saw many smaller brigades merge into larger units. A few of the yellow and white fire engines even survived until their disposal time came during the 1980s Who knows what the decision makers of those days would have thought of the modern-day multicolour schemes and high conspicuity liveries of fire engines seen everywhere across the United Kingdom nowadays?

Brigade on various features and technical specifications, in 1959 Leyland produced the first of four new Firemasters for that busy brigade. Three of Manchester's new Leylands were configured as pump escapes to carry a 55 ft wheeled ladder. Manchester's first Firemaster pump escape was bodied by Carmichael whilst Cocker of Southport built the remaining two. The fourth Firemaster went into service as an emergency tender.

The Firemaster was a truly innovative fire engine. Using many components from the Worldmaster bus chassis, the Firemaster had a front-mounted Sigmund 900 gpm pump, and a horizontally mounted underfloor 9.8-litre six-cylinder C1 diesel engine, driving though a Leyland four-speed semi-automatic epicyclic gearbox. Access to the pump bay was through two hinged opening doors in the lower cab frontage. Another new feature of the Firemaster was the provision of high pressure hose reels capable of providing water fog at up to 500 psi, giving fire crews enormous cooling potential for a minimal water usage.

Unfortunately, the Leyland Firemaster never really took off commercially, for despite some intensive promotional activity, only six other Firemaster orders were received over the next four years. These were for two pump escapes for Glasgow Fire Service (with bodies by David Haydon and Cocker), two as dual-purpose pumps/emergency salvage tenders for Essex County Fire Brigade (bodied by David Haydon), whilst the remaining two on Leyland TFM2 chassis went to Wolverhampton and Darlington Brigades as the bases for Magirus 100ft turntable ladders. The Darlington Firemaster TL did not have a front mounted pump. Both TLs were engineered by David Haydon with some bodywork by Wilsdons.

In 1963, with only a disappointing total of 10 of these very innovative Firemasters in operational service, Leyland finally decided to take their leave of the British fire engine scene. Many fire brigade personnel were left to reflect on the company's proud and historic strength up to the Second World War when for three decades and more, Leyland and Dennis had been the predominant forces in the British fire engine market.

Why the Firemaster never really sold in large numbers is still something of an enigma. Perhaps some sections of the fire service were just too traditional to accept such a radical new concept in fire engine design. Yet more than 40 years on, no fewer than three of the ten Firemasters built are now in preservation – a Glasgow pump escape, the Manchester emergency tender and the Darlington TL

The first Dennis low line F117 Delta chassis/Simon SS65 hydraulic platform produced in 1963 to the specification of Liverpool Fire Brigade. This good looking aerial fire engine served in the front line until 1984 when the Simon booms were re-chassied onto a new Dennis F125 that is still in service with Merseyside Fire Brigade. (Jerry Hepworth)

Two of the 10 Leyland Firemasters delivered in 1963 went to Essex County Fire Brigade as pump/salvage tenders. This view shows the Firemaster attached to Colchester Fire Station at work at an incident. Note the front-mounted pump that was one of the features of these innovative Leylands. (Keith Wardell collection)

This 1971 ERF/HCB Angus pump, now in preservation, saw service in the City of Cardiff Fire Brigade. (Keith Wardell collection)

DEVELOPMENTS AT DENNIS

Meanwhile, events at the Dennis factory could not have been more different. Even though the Guildford-based company were beginning to struggle with their various lorry, bus and coach rivals, their fire engine sales continued to hold up in the face of economic competition from AEC, Bedford, Commer, Karrier, Merryweather and other manufacturers. By early 1960, Dennis were just about to phase out production of two highly successful models, the F8 and F12. The diesel powered F101 and F102 had been well received and the Dennis order book also started to reflect the new F26 and its variants that had been introduced to replace the F12. The new F series models continued the Dennis post-war association with Rolls Royce engines with the F26 being offered with either the 5.7-litre straight eight-cylinder B80 160 bhp or the 195 bhp B81 power units.

Another new Dennis model that set a development benchmark for aerial fire engines was the low line F117 Delta chassis/Simon SS65 hydraulic platform produced in 1963 to the specification of Liverpool Fire Brigade. This new chassis had a driving position set well ahead of the front axle thus allowing the cab to be set considerably lower in order to allow for the mounting of hydraulic platform booms. Over the next few years, Dennis supplied various chassis including the F44, F45, F108 and F123 for marrying to Simon hydraulic platforms. The increasing performance and suitability of HPs for firefighting and rescue operations saw a number of older turntable ladders being replaced by modern HPs, although in many cases city brigades retained turntable ladders for specific risk areas due to their ability to get to work readily in narrow streets.

ERF ARRIVES

Another new British fire engine maker on the street appeared when ERF launched their first fire engine chassis at the 1966 Commercial Motor Show. This was designed as a pump and had bodywork provided by HCB-Angus. Known as the 64PF, the new ERF was powered by a V8 510 Perkins diesel engine and had a rear-mounted 750 gpm pump and 100-gallon water tank. The prototype ERF pump was delivered to Newcastle and Gateshead Joint Fire Service as a pump escape. Later ERF versions offered a Rolls Royce petrol engine and midships mounted pump. The ERF was soon a popular and economic choice and over the next eight years, a total of some 130 ERFs went into service. Of these, 74 were as Simon HPs of various heights ranging from 50 ft to 85 ft.

FAREWELL TO ALBION

One old fire engine name that reappeared in 1966 was that of the Glasgow-based firm, Albion. In 1966, working in conjunction with bodybuilders Carmichael of Worcester, Albion introduced a pump known as the Fire Chief. This was based upon the Albion Chieftain truck chassis using a Leyland 6.5-litre Leyland diesel engine and six-speed gearbox. Unfortunately, by 1968 only a few of these Albions had been sold to fire brigades and before long, the badge disappeared from fire service use.

FANFARE FOR FORD

Ford was another name to enter the fire engine arena in a successful manner when the D series chassis was launched in 1967. The D600 was a relatively low cost chassis and before long was being utilised for a significant number of water tender applications. The first of these boasted bodywork by HCB-Angus, although a number of other fire vehicle bodybuilders worked with the several hundred Ford water tenders commissioned over the next decade. The new Ford D600 came with the six-litre turbo-charged diesel 140 bhp or a 130 bhp petrol version.

By the late 1960s, fire brigades were also beginning to make use of some of the growing number of compact smaller sized vehicles for front line fire service work. By then, the Land Rover was already very well established in many of the rural shire counties in a variety of 4 x 4 light pump and rescue configurations. The newer arrivals on the van scene included examples of the Commer Walk-Thrus, Ford Transits, and Bedford CF. These were converted to serve in various operational roles including rescue and emergency tenders, breathing apparatus units and control vehicles.

GEORDIE MINIS

A few commercial van types were even modified with modest sized inboard water tanks and fitted pumps to become first strike units, particularly in a number of inner city and urban areas where pedestrian schemes were beginning to create access difficulties for full sized appliances. One of the earliest examples of such light vehicle modification was in Newcastle and Gateshead Joint Fire Service. In 1966 the brigade acquired two lightweight mini tenders based upon the Leyland three-quarter ton Atlas chassis built by Standard-Triumph. With a turning circle of less than 30ft, a width of 5 ft 6 in, and an all up weight of less than 3.5 tons, they were ideal small vehicles for the purpose.

Essentially designed to operate as an operational pair, the two Newcastle and Gateshead mini fire engines combined the equivalent equipment of one full-sized water pump. One of these lightweights carried a 45 ft alloy ladder whilst the second ran with a 35 ft wooden extension ladder. Although the two mini fire engines relied on hydrants for their water supply, they both were equipped with inboard transverse pumps.

A serious fire in a warehouse and office block in Shoreditch, London, in October 1959. Crews are working off two wheeled escape ladders, whilst in the left foreground, a 1938 Morris Magirus 100ft turntable ladder begins work. Other classic London Fire Brigade fire engines present include (to the right of the TL) a 1936 Leyland limousine pump; a 1952 Dennis F12 pump escape; a 1952 AEC/Merryweather Regent III pump and (far right) the LFB Control Unit based on a 1937 Leyland coach. The TL continued to serve until 1967 although the 1936 Leyland pump was replaced by a new Dennis only a few months after this photograph.
(Author's collection)

CHAPTER NINE

New Versus Tried And Trusted

Despite an increasing downturn in their lorry and buses sales, in 1968 Dennis Brothers still managed to maintain their historic position as market leaders in fire engines, not just in the United Kingdom but across the Commonwealth and other developing countries.

NEW MODELS FROM GUILDFORD

The various models of the successful Dennis F series were supplemented by the F108 with manual gearbox and turbo-charged Perkins V8 diesel, together with its automatic sister, the F109. 1968 saw this new pair of latest Dennis models joined by a completely new arrival from the Guildford factory, the D series water tender. At only 7 ft wide, the D was particularly designed to appeal to rural brigades where ready access down narrow country lanes was a frequent problem. What was unusual about the Dennis D was the initial choice of power unit – the 4.2 litre petrol Jaguar. However, the first Ds had not long been in operational service when it became evident that this was not suitable for fire engine use. Dennis quickly moved to replace the Jaguar engine with a trusty Rolls Royce B61 unit.

GLASGOW GO GERMAN

1968 was also an ominously significant date for British fire engine builders, for in that year, Glasgow Fire Service caused quite a stir when they ordered four new 50 ft wheeled pump escapes on the German built Magirus Deutz 150D chassis. Although these pump escapes were bodied by local company Scottish Motor Transport Ltd, they were in fact the first non-British chassis used for British fire engines for operational service in a United Kingdom fire brigade since before

the Second World War. Two years later, Glasgow ordered three more Magirus Deutz chassis as the bases for new 100 ft Magirus turntable ladders. Given the almost total European chassis domination of fire engines throughout modern-day British brigades, it could be argued that the arrival of these German Deutzes on Glasgow fire stations more than three decades ago was the beginning of the end for the truly all-British-built fire engine.

Although Dennis continued to achieve commercial success with its fire engine range, the company was increasingly struggling to survive in the general commercial vehicle market. As a result, in 1972 Dennis was the subject of a takeover by the Hestair Group, following which some loss making areas and a part of its huge Guildford factory were sold off in an effort to stay profitable.

FAREWELL TO AEC

Into the 1970s, other manufacturers were under similar pressure and experiencing mixed fortunes. For 10 years, the AEC company had been part of the British Leyland conglomerate and since then, an AEC chassis had been the choice of many brigades for a large number of new or re-chassied Merryweather, Magirus or Metz turntable ladders.

This County Borough of Hastings Merryweather 100ft turntable ladder was one of the 100 or so AEC fire engines built on the Mercury TGM chassis with the Ergonomic cab. The Hastings TL was one of the last series of AECs and went into service in 1967. It passed into the ownership of East Sussex Fire Brigade before being retired in 1990. (Jerry Hepworth)

In 1967 AEC first utilised its new Ergonomic cab for a fire service pumping application, and various bodybuilders using the Mercury TGM chassis built about 100 AECs with Ergonomic cabs. These included some 20 Merryweather TLs, 10 specials of various types and a number of pumps.

Unfortunately, despite the interest in the Ergonomic cab and its widespread use in the early 1970s for a range of other Leyland commercial vehicles, the Ergonomic cab TGM chassis were destined to be AEC's last foray into fire engines. It is likely that AEC were finding cost competition from the likes of Dennis, Bedford, ERF, Dodge and the newly arrived Ford chassis just about the last straw.

SCOTTISH SCOOSHERS SET THE SCENE

Apart from Glasgow's foray into Deutz pump escapes one year earlier, a most innovative new fire engine of 1969 were the three Scooshers introduced by Glasgow Fire Service. (The term Scoosher comes from an old Glaswegian word for a water pistol). The Mk I Scooshers were essentially an aerial firefighting unit mounted on a Dennis D chassis with two articulated hydraulic booms supplied by Simon. The head of the booms were fitted with a remotely controlled Angus monitor (branch), whose purpose was to project a firefighting jet into the upper floors of a burning building where immediate access for firefighters was likely to be difficult. The Mk I Scoosher was also fitted with an infra-red sensor and a window-breaking device. Their overall working height was 32 ft.

The new Glasgow aerial fire engine attracted a lot of national

The City of Sheffield Fire Brigade were one of several urban brigades who used the AEC Mercury with Ergonomic cab as a water tender ladder. Now in preservation, this 1970 former Sheffield AEC is seen at a rally with a fine array of ladders apart from its principal 45 ft version.
(Keith Wardell collection)

attention and must have been operationally successful in the Scottish city, for over the next four years, Glasgow Fire Service added a further 11 Scooshers to its fleet. 1970 saw the delivery of the first of five larger MK II versions, each with 45 ft Simon booms mounted on a rotating turntable. These MK IIs were built on the Dennis F46A chassis whilst a further six Glasgow Mk IIa Scooshers mounted on the Dodge K850 chassis went into operational service some two years later. The Mk I and II Scooshers were bodied by Bennett's of Glasgow and the Mk IIa by Carmichael.

LIVERPOOL GETS IN ON THE ACT

Soon after the arrival of the first Glasgow Scooshers, other fire brigades began to explore the likely operational potential of this new type of aerial vehicle. In 1971, Liverpool Fire Brigade took delivery of a 42 ft Simonitor. This, a variation on the Glasgow Scoosher, was mounted on an extended Dennis F49 chassis. Unlike the Scooshers, Liverpool's Simonitor had a single telescopic hydraulic boom on which was fitted a remotely controlled monitor, with the booms able to carry a weight equivalent to four persons.

Yet another example of the AEC Mercury with Ergonomic cab is this pump escape of the City of Nottingham Fire Brigade. New in 1971, it had bodywork by HCB Angus and subsequently served operationally with the enlarged Nottinghamshire Fire and Rescue Service until the late 1980s. (Jerry Hepworth)

An unusual view taken c.1980 of a 1971 Dennis F109 of the London Fire Brigade during a recruits' drill session at Training School. This F109 was one of a batch of 18 designed to LFB specification. Here the 45 ft wooden wheeled escape ladder is about to be slipped and pitched to the drill tower. Note the two wooden LFB-style hook ladders and first floor ladder. (Keith Wardell collection)

One year later, Lancashire County Fire Brigade were clearly persuaded of the value of the Simonitor when they ordered a similar model to Liverpool's, although theirs was mounted on a Ford D1616 chassis with bodywork provided by HCB Angus. Both these new Simonitors had built-in escape ladders running alongside their booms and the Lancashire version was actually designated as a foam tender, as it was capable of discharging foam from its head. Lancashire ordered a second identical Ford Simonitor in 1972.

Over the next four years, a total of eight more Simonitors were commissioned by brigades including West Riding, Essex County, County of Flintshire, Manchester, Durham and Hampshire. History records that although most of the Scooshers and Simonitors had operational lives of around 10 years, the experience gained in the use of these fire engines undoubtedly contributed to subsequent developments in aerial ladder design and hydraulic technology, leading towards taller and more effective hydraulic platforms and the arrival of the first aerial ladder platforms.

A RADICAL REORGANISATION

In 1974 came a major reorganisation of local government, one that was to have a profound effect on public British fire brigades and their work. The merger of a number of city and county borough brigades created six large urban metropolitan brigades. The new metropolitan brigades included West Midlands, South Yorkshire, West Yorkshire, Greater Manchester, Merseyside, and Tyne and Wear (London had undergone a similar exercise in 1965 when the London Fire Brigade joined with all of the Middlesex, Croydon, East Ham, West Ham Brigades, and parts of Surrey, Kent, Essex and Hertfordshire to form an enlarged Greater London Fire Brigade).

The 1974 reorganisation saw similar amalgamations across the rural shire counties and the number of British public brigades was reduced from a post-war total of 147 to 65. All this had a significant effect on the fire engine fleets of different brigades. Overnight, some found themselves with strange bedfellows, with instances of old all-diesel brigades suddenly incorporating quite a few petrol-engined water tenders in the fleet. The new larger brigades also now included a disparate range of turntable ladders and other aerials and specials such as emergency tenders, foam tenders and hose layers, not a few of which dated from the 1950s. Notwithstanding the national JCDD specifications, the 1974 reorganisation meant that it was to be quite a few years before the enlarged fire engine fleets took on some form of standardisation to reflect the operational preferences of a particular enlarged brigade.

THE ARRIVAL OF THE PACESETTER

Another interesting specific technical fire engine development of the mid 1970s was the arrival in 1975 of the Chubb Pacesetter. The origins of the Pacesetter can be traced back to 1969 and a fire engine design project with particular emphasis on firefighter crew safety undertaken by Loughborough Consultants Ltd, a company set up by Loughborough University.

Working in collaboration with Chubb Fire Security Ltd, the Loughborough project team analysed data relating to fire service accident statistics and gradually evolved the ergonomics and engineering specification of a radically new water tender design. With the active involvement of Merseyside Fire Brigade, a specification was finally worked up in late 1974, and the build of the new Chubb Pacesetter began.

The Pacesetter was based upon a Reynolds Boughton Scorpio chassis with a rear-mounted 238 bhp V6 Detroit Diesel engine and Allison automatic four-speed transmission. Rated at 10 tons, this new water tender was certainly a quick fire engine, with a top speed of 75 mph and an acceleration of 0 to 40 mph in just 18 seconds. With a fire engineering layout somewhat similar to the commercially unsuccessful 1959 series Leyland Firemaster pumps, the Pacesetter sported a 450-gallon fibreglass water tank and a front-mounted 1,000 gpm Godiva pump accessible through a panel in the vehicle's front. A particular feature of the Pacesetter was its six-man integral easy access crew cab built of light alloy and fibreglass. The cab had a step height of only 18 inches and was accessible through a three-fold power-operated door, with the low line being continued along the body sides, allowing low level lockers and 45 ft ladder mountings.

Despite a high-profile launch, the Chubb Pacesetter was not

One of the very successful Carmichael Commando 6 × 4 Range Rover conversions designed to provide a fast response light firefighting and rescue tender. This Commando went into service with Hertfordshire Fire Brigade in 1975 as a rescue tender and was based initially at Hatfield, later moving to Garston. (Author's collection)

commercially successful, with only two being sold. One of these went into service with Merseyside Fire Brigade whilst the second joined the fleet at the then Fire Service Technical College, at Moreton in Marsh in Gloucestershire.

LAND ROVER WORKHORSES

For some years, many rural fire brigades had been increasingly using the basic Land Rover 4 x 4 as light pumps. These regularly proved their worth as reliable workhorses in all weather, day and night.

Although the open-back l09-inch wheelbase Land Rover continued to be a proven and reliable performer in rural firefighting and rescue situations from Lands End to John'O Groats, the growing number of serious road crashes on the developing motorway network saw fire brigades beginning to look elsewhere for a very fast response rescue/emergency tender with a reasonable equipment payload.

STRETCHING THE RANGE ROVER

By the early 1970s, several brigades were evaluating the newly introduced Range Rover as a possible solution to this particular operational light vehicle problem. With its 3.5-litre V8 petrol engine, the Range Rover was undoubtedly fast, but its standard payload and carrying space, together with the need for a provision of some firefighting water, presented something of an engineering challenge.

Carmichael of Worcester eventually provided the innovative answer with the provision of a patented design that added a trailing third axle, significantly increasing the overall payload capacity. Dubbed the Commando, some 37 of these 6 x 4 Range Rover light fire engines were delivered over a six-year period from 1972. Range Rover Commandos went into service with brigades that included Surrey, Bedfordshire,

Somerset, West Sussex, Cornwall, Northern Area (Scotland), Mid Glamorgan and Clwyd (Wales).

The Commandos featured enclosed rear stowage using a transverse through locker with roller shutters. Various equipment options included a powerful front-mounted winch and 200 gpm Godiva pump with a 200-gallon inboard water tank for both firefighting water and foam. In a rescue tender configuration, many Range Rovers had a PTO-driven generator providing electrical power for various cutting and spreading tools together with a telescopic mast floodlighting system.

The Commando Range Rovers were truly stylish looking light fire engines with a scintillating performance to match, capable of exceeding 80 mph even when fully loaded, and were almost certainly the most rapid fire engines in the British fire service at that time. Not surprisingly, they were much liked by drivers lucky enough to get their hands on these fine machines.

1973 saw the first of a number of these Range Rover 6 x 4 conversions built by the Gloster Saro company to the order of the Ministry of Defence for RAF airfield duty to serve as rapid intervention vehicles. These airfield Range Rovers differed from the Carmichael version in that they had a four-door cab to accommodate a crew of up to four firefighters.

MANCHESTER'S MONSTER 6 x 6

1973 also saw the first British order for a new generation of heavy airfield crash tenders known as the Pathfinder. Destined for Manchester Airport, this 35-ton monster was manufactured by Chubb Fire Security on a Reynolds Boughton rear-engined 6 x 6 Griffin chassis. Powered by a V16 Detroit Diesel developing a massive 635 bhp, it boasted a central driving position and five-man crew accommodation. The Pathfinder carried 3,000 gallons of water and 360 gallons of foam compound. Its huge cab rooftop monitor could throw over 13,500 gpm of foam across a distance of some 300ft.

FIREBALL IN SUNDERLAND

Our photograph captures a very dramatic moment during firefighting operations in Sunderland in 1972. The crew of this ERF pump of Sunderland Fire Brigade were called to smoke issuing from a shop in the centre of Sunderland and upon their arrival pitched a ladder to the first floor flat above the shop and got a hose reel to work. Without warning, there was a flashover within the shop which blew out the glass shop front, sending flames upwards to engulf the extension ladder and floor above. The ferocity of the fireball even set fire to the nearside bodywork of the ERF. Fortunately, none of the crew was seriously hurt and reinforcing pumps were soon on the scene to bring the blaze under control. *(Jim Bryce)*

CHAPTER TEN

Competition Takes Its Toll

In the early 1970s Dennis Brothers, the most long standing and prominent builder of British pumping fire engines, were still having to work hard to stave off the increasing commercial competition for fire engine business from Bedford, Dodge, ERF and Ford.

It certainly did not help matters when in 1975, a new name on the British fire engine scene arrived in the form of Shelvoke and Drewry (S and D). In collaboration with Carmichael bodybuilders of Worcester, a prototype S and D water tender was launched using the WX chassis. Over the next few years, a number of S and D's water tenders and pumps appeared using the WX chassis, with the heavier WY chassis becoming the base for turntable ladders, hydraulic platforms and other special vehicles for a wide range of brigades.

DENNIS'S BOLD RESPONSE

Dennis felt their fortunes lay with the latest F108 and F109 series models that had been introduced in 1968. However, by the early 1970s this pair had been technically refined about as far as was practical without a major redesign. All this was against a background where Dennis found their vehicle cost base increasing alarmingly; in particular the integral cab used on the F series with its aluminium covered ash frame was expensive and time-consuming to build.

Thus in 1976 Dennis boldly launched a new model – the R series water tender. This utilised a brand new contoured glass fibre cab mounted on an F series chassis with an uprated air-braked system. Powered by a choice of either Perkins V8 540 or 640 diesels, the Dennis R quickly became popular, especially with county fire brigades. So successful was the R series that within two years Dennis were enjoying over 40% of

JUL 57D, a 1965 AEC Mercury Merryweather 100 ft turntable ladder was one of six delivered new in that year to the London Fire Brigade to replace older TLs in the brigade's fleet. First attached to G25 West Hampstead Fire Station, it was transferred to A21 Paddington in 1972 where it served until being finally sold out of service in 1986. (Keith Wardell collection)

British fire engine market share.

The R series was only available with a Perkins diesel power unit which meant that the new model finally broke a historic link with the petrol engine since the very first Dennis fire engines left the Guildford factory almost 70 years earlier.

THE END OF ERF

Soon after the successful 1976 launch of the R series, Dennis must have been doubly delighted when it was learnt that ERF had taken the unexpected decision, as had Leyland back in 1963, to discontinue fire engine manufacture to allow for a concentration on the truck market. However, this turned out to be a rather long-winded commercial withdrawal as Cheshire Fire Engineering (CFE), ERF's bodybuilding trading company, continued to build and deliver ERF fire engines during the lengthy period that the parent company tried to find a buyer for the concern.

This exercise continued to prove unsuccessful until 1982, when ERF formally wound up the CFE company. However, almost immediately a number of former CFE employees formed Saxon SVB Ltd with the initial aim of producing parts for ERF fire engines with a subsequent aim to compete for new build opportunities. Two years later, the new company, still based at Sandbach, changed its name to Saxon Sanbec Ltd, and grew to become a prominent British manufacturer using a wide range of chassis in their fire engine build programme.

DENNIS BACK A WINNER

Back at the Dennis factory at Guildford, the company were delighted by the buoyant success of the R series, yet were also increasingly conscious of the need for stronger and more robust cabs for fire engines. Dennis consequently embarked on a plan for an all-steel safety cab that was eventually designed on their behalf by Ogle. The new safety cab first went into production in 1979 at a section of the Dennis factory specially modified to produce the new assembly. By the end of that year, the new cab had been fitted to a modified R series pump and the prototype RS was born.

Like the R, the RS was powered by a choice of Perkins V8 diesels, and was fitted with Girling Skidcheck anti-lock brakes as standard, making it one of the first British fire engines to feature such technology. Dennis also produced a tilt cab version titled the SS model together with a compact 7 ft width rural model called the DS. Greater Manchester County Fire Service was the launch customer for the RS, with 14 water tender ladders designated as the RS 131. These Manchester RSs were fitted with the increasingly popular Allison automatic gearbox and many other brigades soon followed suit with orders for the RS, SS and DS models.

Dennis quickly realised they had a winner on their hands, and over the next decade and more, the RS, SS and DS went on to become the most successful fire engines ever to be built by Dennis. The RS and SS models continued to be manufactured right up until early 1995 by which time a total number of 1,750 had left the Guildford factory. These were delivered not just to British fire brigades but to fire and rescue organisations in various parts of the world. Many of these RS and SS models have stood the test of time and a number are still in active operational service in various guises.

UPGRADES FOR DODGE

In late 1978, Dodge introduced new chassis, the G13 and heavier G16 series. These replaced their K850 chassis, much used for a number of water tenders, and its heavier sister K1050 version, utilised for quite a few early Simon hydraulic platforms. These new Dodge models continued to be popular as a preferred economic choice by a number of urban and shire county brigades for both water tender and high-rise vehicle applications.

DEMOUNTABLES DESCEND

This was also the period when the first demountable operational units really came into vogue. One of the first UK brigades to introduce demountables was Oxfordshire. In 1978, they commissioned a

Powell Duffryn Rolonoff system together with a Bedford TK prime mover. Suffolk Fire Service followed in the same year using the same demountable system with separate pods providing four operational functions: chemical incident, control, breathing apparatus, and foam units. Across in Wales, Mid Glamorgan Fire Service had also adopted Rolonof pods, although their prime movers were on the Ford 1010 chassis.

THE FIRST SCANIA

1981 was another significant date marking the arrival of yet another foreign chassis for use in the British fire service. The first 'fire' Scania chassis, a low line LB81 powered by a 7.8-litre 190 bhp diesel, was destined for Grampian Fire Brigade as the base for a new Metz DLK 30-metre turntable ladder built by Angloco of Batley. Grampian's new TL also featured an innovative onboard computer to assist in fault finding, and was also fitted with a cage at its head replete with floodlighting and a provision for power tool use during aerial rescue work.

Few involved in fire and rescue service vehicles would have thought that within three years, this first Scania would be joined by increasing numbers of other makes of foreign chassis in the fleets of British brigades, including both Mercedes Benz and Volvo. In fact such was the incessant displacement of British fire vehicles by the new overseas arrivals that by the end of the decade Volvo were able to demonstrate that they enjoyed over a 40% market share of new British pumping fire engines.

S AND D DEPART

The arrival of the first new British Scania also heralded the departure of another British fire engine chassis manufacturer when Shelvoke and Drewry took the decision to depart from the fire and rescue vehicle scene. From about 1983 onwards, only a relative few new S and Ds were delivered, mostly turntable ladders and hydraulic platforms bodied by Angloco, Carmichael and Saxon Sanbec.

PLATFORMS TAKE OFF

Bearing in mind that the first British firefighting hydraulic platform – a Commer VAC/Simon SS 65-foot model – was only delivered to Monmouthshire Fire Brigade in 1963, it is interesting to record that within 15 years, British fire brigades had generally embraced the hydraulic platform for operational high-rise firefighting and rescue work.

By the early 1980s the numbers of HPs in commission compared to turntable ladders had grown to become fairly well balanced. Even the somewhat conservative London Fire Brigade (LFB), who at that time ran no fewer than 29 100 ft TLs with a number in reserve, purchased

LONDON'S BURNING

This action-packed photograph taken in 1963 shows several B Division crews of the London Fire Brigade at work at a six-pump fire in a general warehouse in the district known as Dockhead, a close-packed area of streets running along the south bank of the Thames above Tower Bridge towards Bermondsey and the Surrey Docks. Many warehouses were a feature of this high fire-risk area of London, and not far away was the site of the huge Tooley Street conflagration of 1861 that claimed the life of the Brigade's famous Chief Officer, James Braidwood.

In this view, Station 63 Dockhead's 50 ft wheeled escape has been pitched into the second floor and two firemen at its head are attempting to open up a double door known as a loophole. On an adjacent escape ladder from a supporting station, (probably 62 Southwark), a crew rigged in Proto oxygen breathing apparatus sets make their entry into the smoke of the burning building with a charged hose line. Both escape ladders have been let out in their carriage frames to reduce the steepness of their working angle.

Note the gleaming condition of Dockhead's AEC Regent Pump Escape and its well polished and varnished wooden hook ladders. The goods packages apparently crammed into the first floor of the building give some clue as to the likely conditions inside the premises. Such medium-sized warehouse incidents were relatively commonplace in this LFB area at this time, and this fire would probably have been a bread and butter job for these experienced inner London crews.

In more recent times, Dockhead Fire Station's claim to fame is that it was where the *London's Burning* TV series was based, although in the series it was known as Blackwall Fire Station. *(London Fire Brigade)*

Another typical water tender of the late 1970s is this 1979 Dodge G1313 HCB/ Angus of Gwent Fire Brigade, now also in preservation. (Keith Wardell collection)

two 75 ft Simon SS models for evaluation. One of these was mounted on an ERF 84PS chassis whilst the second was married to a Dennis F123. London Fire Brigade must have been pretty impressed by the performance of these HPs, because in 1982 the capital's fire brigade acquired a further 15, soon to become the LFB's predominant type of aerial fire engine. All the new aerials were Simon SS220 models built on Dennis F125, Dodge G16 and Shelvoke and Drewry WY chassis.

DEMISE OF AN ERA

With the London order under their belt, Simon continued to consolidate and develop its position as the primary British supplier of HPs, although it was a different story with Merryweather, the only remaining British manufacturer of turntable ladders. Merryweather were the oldest fire engineering company in the United Kingdom and their fire engine manufacturing pedigree could be readily traced back to around 1750. The company had manufactured some of the first manual fire engine equipment, before going on to become one of the world's predominant builders of steam pumps, into the 20th century motor age and their many years of turntable ladder expertise.

Sadly, by the early 1980s, Merryweather had suffered considerable retrenchment under various ownerships and were clearly losing out commercially to aggressive marketing from the two principal German TL builders, Metz and Magirus, whose new products increasingly appeared in British fire brigades. In 1983, Merryweather received an order from Strathclyde Fire Brigade for what was to be the last British-built TL. This was for the Merryweather XRL model mounted on a Commer G16C chassis. Shortly after the delivery of this aerial fire engine, the parent company finally closed the books on Merryweather, a company who had earned a revered name and historic place in British fire engine history.

TONS OF TRANSITS

Although the use of Ford chassis for water tender and special vehicle use was declining by the early 1980s, the Ford badge grew increasingly popular at the smaller end of the fire vehicle scale. The Ford Transit in its various wheelbase forms particularly lent itself to a wide range of applications, such as damage control unit (Surrey), breathing apparatus tenders and control units (London), and salvage tender (Hertfordshire). By 1984, a whole clutch of rescue tenders using the heavier Transit chassis had joined the fleets of a number of brigades including South Yorkshire, Strathclyde and Surrey.

Since their introduction in 1974, the numbers of Ford A series chassis had seen widespread use as rescue/emergency tenders. This model Ford's sturdy construction and 3.5-ton payload enabled an ever-growing amount of cutting and lifting rescue gear and associated equipment to be carried. By the time of the demise of the A series chassis almost 10 years later, no fewer than 66 Ford As were in operational use in English, Scottish and Welsh brigades.

A SHORT-LIVED NEWCOMER

Another interesting medium-sized fire engine development of this time was the Stonefield P5000 4 x 4 and 6 x 4 all-terrain vehicle. The company was set up in 1976 in Scotland with some government assistance, with the aim of helping to reinvigorate the vehicle industry in that part of the country. Over a period of four years, a total of six P5000s were delivered as rescue/emergency tenders to Strathclyde, Grampian, Lothian and Borders and Humberside brigades, with Cambridgeshire taking a pair. The Stonefield featured an integral body and was powered by a 5.2-litre V8 petrol engine driving through a three-speed automatic gearbox. Unhappily, no further P5000s were sold into the British fire service and in 1992 the badge disappeared from the British fire scene with the withdrawal from service of the last of these rugged-looking fire engines.

An example of Dennis's most successful fire engines, the RS and SS series first introduced in 1979. This SS 131 (with tilt cab) was delivered in 1984 to the London Fire Brigade and was one of 108 such Dennis pumps built for the capital's brigade. (Keith Wardell collection)

CHAPTER ELEVEN

Towards The End Of The Century

By the early 1990s, the British fire engine scene was being increasingly dominated by European chassis manufacturers. These included Iveco, Mercedes-Benz, Scania and Volvo, all of whom continued to win a market share from the few remaining British suppliers. This situation was not helped at all by the continuing economic pressure on fire brigade budgets.

In 1990 the predominant British manufacturer, Dennis Specialist Vehicles, ended an era of building a complete pumping fire engine to concentrate on only building fire engine, bus and coach chassis cabs. However, in conjunction with John Dennis Coachbuilders came the Dennis Rapier. This new fire engine body incorporated innovative composite material panels instead of plywood and was mounted upon a tubular stainless steel chassis and emphasised the move towards greater levels of crew safety being built into new fire engine design.

This was also a time of development in high-rise firefighting and rescue fire engines. The arrival of the aerial ladder platform (ALP) saw the merging of the original functions of the turntable ladder with the hydraulic platform to provide a more versatile specialist fire engine. The ALPs were increasingly mounted on large 6 x 4 and even 8 x 4 chassis to provide the stability and anchorage for their increasing working heights and projection.

EUROPEAN STANDARDS

Another significant development of this period concurrent with the growth of the European Union was the establishment of Euro standards for firefighting equipment through the CEN committee structure. The effect of this was the final demise of the historical

Opposite, top: This view is of a typical 4 x 4 airport foam tender (FT) from the late 1990s and has bodywork by Carmichael on a Scania 124C 420 chassis. The high ground clearance provides for an all-terrain capability. (Jerry Hepworth)

Opposite, below: This larger capacity Carmichael Cobra 2 6 x 6 foam tender (FT) went new into operational service at Belfast City Airport. (Jerry Hepworth)

British JCCD specifications that had served the fire service and the British fire engine manufacturers so well since their creation in 1948.

During this time, the increasing social problems of some urban areas began to create real difficulties for fire crews in securing fire engines and their host of on-board valuable firefighting and rescue equipment. As a result, the design of new fire vehicles increasingly incorporated central locking arrangements, not just for the crew cab itself but for all the equipment lockers as well.

CONSORTIUM PURCHASING

With unrelenting financial pressures on fire service budgets, a number of fire authorities came together to form a purchasing consortium for various equipment including the specification of a standard water tender. This specification eventually emerged to include a 1,818-litre water tank, a Godiva 2500 pump, and the provision for various ladders including a 13.5-metre and shorter general-purpose version together with a roof ladder. However, there was some flexibility over the locker stowage and a number of sliding trays allowed for a brigade's local preference for the on-board layout of the considerable amount of firefighting and rescue equipment being carried by front-line fire engines. The outcome of the work of the consortium was the Dennis Sabre chassis with bodywork by John Dennis Coachbuilders. The first of these water tenders was delivered to Wiltshire Fire & Rescue Service in 1995.

In 1980, London Fire Brigade introduced the first of a series of new high-rise fire engines based upon the Volvo FL6-18 chassis with a Simon SS220 30-metre hydraulic platform (HP). These were in the operational front line in the capital until the late 1990s. When introduced these HPs typified British high-rise firefighting and rescue vehicle design at that time. (London Fire Brigade)

A colourful and impressive line-up of three London Fire Brigade fire engines from the latter years of the 20th century. From left to right they are a Volvo FL6-18 Simon SS220 30 metre HP and two Volvo FL6-14 pumps (designated pump ladders: PLs), typical of the workhorses of the capital's fire brigade of that time. (London Fire Brigade)

One of a pair new in 1997 to Lancashire County Fire Brigade was this 32-metre Bronto Skylift aerial ladder platform (ALP). Mounted on a Volvo FL10 6 x 4 chassis with bodywork by Angloco, this fire engine was allocated to Preston Fire Station. (Lancashire Fire & Rescue Service)

During the last decade of the 20th century, there was an increasing move towards the preservation of specific classic British fire engines. A leading example of these was the restoration by Mike Hebard of his 1937 101 ft Leyland Metz turntable ladder (TL). Supplied new to the London Fire Brigade and stationed at Soho, this TL saw much active service right through the Blitz years before final retirement and disposal in 1963. Acquired by Mike in 1981 and lovingly restored to its original condition, the Leyland subsequently appeared at the 1983 Royal Tournament and at St. Paul's Cathedral for the 1990 commemorative service to mark the 50th Anniversary of the London Blitz. (Mike Hebard)

Opposite, top: A second example of the first-class restoration of a historic British fire engine is OXT 779, a rare AEC emergency tender (ET) originally commissioned by the London Fire Brigade in 1953 on a Regent Mk III chassis. The restoration was led by former London firefighter Eric Billingham and this photograph shows the AEC ET after a long period of restorative work back to its original pristine condition with both electric and hand-rung bells, long before the days of blue warning beacons and two-tone horns.
(Eric Billingham)

Yet another fine example of British fire engine restoration in the last decade of the century is this former London Fire Brigade 1967 Dennis F106 pump escape. Owned by Norman Simmons, this splendid example carries a 50-foot wooden wheeled escape and is complete with all its original firefighting equipment down to the last detail. This beautifully restored British fire engine regularly appears at fire engine rallies during the summer months. (Fire Services National Museum Trust)

There is always something dramatic about a fire station, especially at night. This is a 1997 view of A21 Paddington Fire Station, one of London's busiest operational units. The doors of the various fire engines are open ready for their firefighting and rescue crews to climb on board and head off to their next emergency 999 call. (London Fire Brigade)

Introduced by Dennis in 1995 as a successor to the popular RS and SS models from the Guildford factory, the Sabre quickly established itself in a number of brigades. Here the prototype is seen under test during acceleration and hill-climb assessments. (Dennis Fire)

Below: Wiltshire was one of the first brigades to commission the new Sabre as water tender ladders (WrL/Rescue). This is one of six such Sabres introduced in the county during 1996, all with bodywork by John Dennis and this view demonstrates the compact design of the equipment stowage of the modern British fire engine. (Wiltshire Fire & Rescue Service)

*Kent Fire Brigade also have a
considerable fleet of Dennis pumps,
both Sabres and the earlier Rapier
and SS models running either as
water tenders (WrTs) or as rescue
water ladders (RWrL). Here a
1994 Rapier poses with a low-line
Iveco Magirus turntable ladder.
(Kent Fire & Rescue Service)*

*Below: A view from the rear of
Stanmore Fire Station of London
Fire Brigade taken in the early
1980s showing both pump escape
(right) and pump turning out to a
daytime emergency.
(London Fire Brigade)*

CHAPTER TWELVE

New Concepts, New Ideas And Fresh Challenges

The arrival of the new century saw an increasing number of British fire brigades utilising very different, and in some cases startling, high-conspicuity liveries for new fire engines coming into service to replace older and outdated fire vehicles, some of which were 15 years old and more. With fire crews attending an increasing number of road crashes with persons trapped in the compacted wreckage, it was important to provide the maximum levels of safety for firefighters working at the scenes of accidents. Stripes, chequerboard effects and even an all-white livery emerged, all somewhat reminiscent of the bold move by Coventry Fire Brigade to break the mould of all-red fire engines back in 1973.

New fire engine bodies using polymer technology were also on the increase, with London Fire Brigade and Lancashire Fire & Rescue Service taking delivery of significant numbers of pumps with moulded bodywork. These were increasingly attractive to fire authorities as the moulded bodywork was extremely robust in operational service and was free from the corrosion problems which had been a concern with some makes in past years.

THE AFTERMATH OF 9/11

The dreadful terrorist attacks in America on 11th September 2001 had far-reaching effects upon the operational vehicle response of the British Fire Service. Very soon after this United States disaster, the British government called for a review of the ability of the UK emergency services to respond to a disaster on such a vast scale. The outcome was the provision by the British government to fire brigades around the country of a large number of MAN 6 x 4 prime movers with demountable incident support units carrying portable decontamination equipment, foam supplies, and a high volume water pumping capacity. Since their introduction, these units have more than proved their worth at a number of major fires and have become particularly valuable during periods of wild weather and serious flooding in various parts of the country.

DEVELOPMENTS IN SPECIALIST FIRE ENGINES

As the operational work of the fire service continued to see an increase in non-fire emergency calls such as road crashes, machinery accidents and chemical and hazardous material incidents, so some fire brigades continued to maintain specialist vehicles such as rescue tenders (RT) or Hazardous Material Units where the vehicle design and equipment carried on board was tailored to specific emergency operations. However some brigades, including London, merged the rescue tender role with that of a pump. In addition to hose, on-board water, breathing apparatus and ladders, these fire engines also provide a wide range of hydraulic cutting, lifting (air bags) and spreading equipment for a wide range of rescue at accident sites.

This was also the time when fire engines and fire service utility vehicles were increasingly carrying prominent eye-catching messages to the community on their side and rear panels, reflecting the growing role of operational crews in promoting safety and prevention with the aim of reducing the number of fire outbreaks.

Several brigades have recently introduced entirely new concepts to the operational scene. Merseyside launched a motorcycle response in its urban areas to try to overcome the ever-growing problem of delays in attendance at the scene of incidents caused by traffic congestion in peak-time hours.

ALL-TERRAIN GROUNDBREAKER

In 2008, Lancashire Fire and Rescue Service introduced a new all-terrain tracked vehicle, the Softrak, specifically for dealing with protracted fires in woods and moorlands during long periods of dry weather. This provided a hugely effective new asset for Lancashire firefighters; the task of getting a conventional 10-tonne pumping fire engine into a moorland situation can frequently be difficult and time consuming. In contrast, the Softrak can get to work quickly in such environments, and in addition to its cross-country capability, carries 1,000 litres of water and can pump water from external supplies such as ponds and streams.

The constant pressures on fire authorities concerning the funding for modern replacements for worn-out and outdated firefighting and rescue vehicles has led to an increase in the number of leasing schemes that provide for a steady planned replacement of older fire engines.

Concurrent with this, the new century has seen the consolidation of an even wider range of European chassis providing the base for new British fire engines. Sad to say, the day of the once-thriving British fire engine industry has gone, even though a small number of specialist bodybuilders remain, continuing to supply the necessary skills and modern engineering techniques to marry a suitable chassis to a fire brigade's preferred cab and body design.

Thankfully, a small number of British fire engines built over the past century have been faithfully restored and preserved by dedicated enthusiasts, and many of these classic vehicles can still be regularly seen at public events in full glorious working order. These magnificent preserved examples serve as a modest reminder of the golden days of the British fire engine, and of the huge contribution that these magnificent vehicles have made to the fire defence of the nation in both peace and war.

In 1966 the London Fire Brigade celebrated 100 years of service. In November of that year, the Queen reviewed the LFB at a display ceremony at Lambeth Headquarters. Here some weeks before is a rare image of eight of London's 29 AEC Merryweather 100 ft turntable ladders rehearsing their part in the Royal Review. This unique drill culminated in the breaking out of the Union flag high over Lambeth.
(London Fire Brigade)

An early example of a turntable ladder in service with the London Fire Brigade, c1921. Mounted on a Leyland chassis, this 85ft TL had wooden extensions and was extended and rotated by hand.

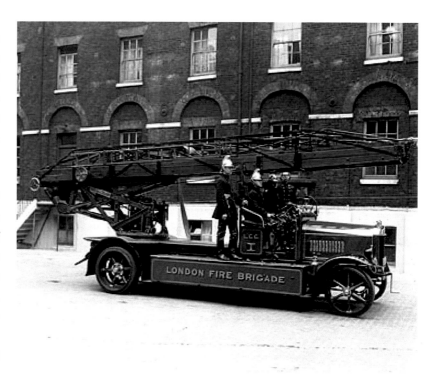

Below: A 1968 Dennis F108 pump escape of the London Fire Brigade pictured in the drill yard of A21 Paddington fire station, immortalised in Gordon's Honeycombe's book Red Watch, which recalls the true dramatic story of the Worsley hotel fire of 1974. (London Fire Brigade)

Before previous page: The new
century increasingly saw several
brigades using innovative liveries
for their fire engines to improve the
safety and conspicuity of personnel
and fire engines at emergency
incidents. This water tender of
Bedfordshire Fire and Rescue
Service sports full-width blue
lights and distinctive striped livery
and is based upon a Scania 260
94D chassis with bodywork by
Emergency One.
(Author's collection)

Previous page: In the late 1990s
Grampian Fire Brigade in Scotland
adopted a somewhat unusual but
striking all-white livery for their fire
engines as illustrated by this Scania
230 94D water tender. The white
background is enhanced with bright
yellow reflective stripes.
(Author's collection)

Hampshire Fire and Rescue Service
are a brigade who have preferred a
more traditional red and polished
aluminium sides design for their
water tenders, which use a Volvo
FL6 14 chassis.
(Author's collection)

Another variation of modern-day distinctive and high-visibility fire engine liveries is this Staffordshire Fire and Rescue Service Scania 260 94D water tender with its red and yellow chequerboard finish. Bodywork is by Emergency One. (Author's collection)

Over page: Following the terrorist attack on New York in September 2001, the British Fire Service re-examined its ability and capacity to deal with such disasters on a huge scale. On the fire engine front the outcome was the government issue, commencing in 2004, of a large number of prime movers designed to transport incident support, high volume pumping capacity and other specialist equipment in demountable units. The prime movers were based on an MAN 6 x 4 chassis with bodywork by Marshall SV. This view shows a long line of MAN prime movers immediately before their issue to various UK fire brigades. (Author's collection)

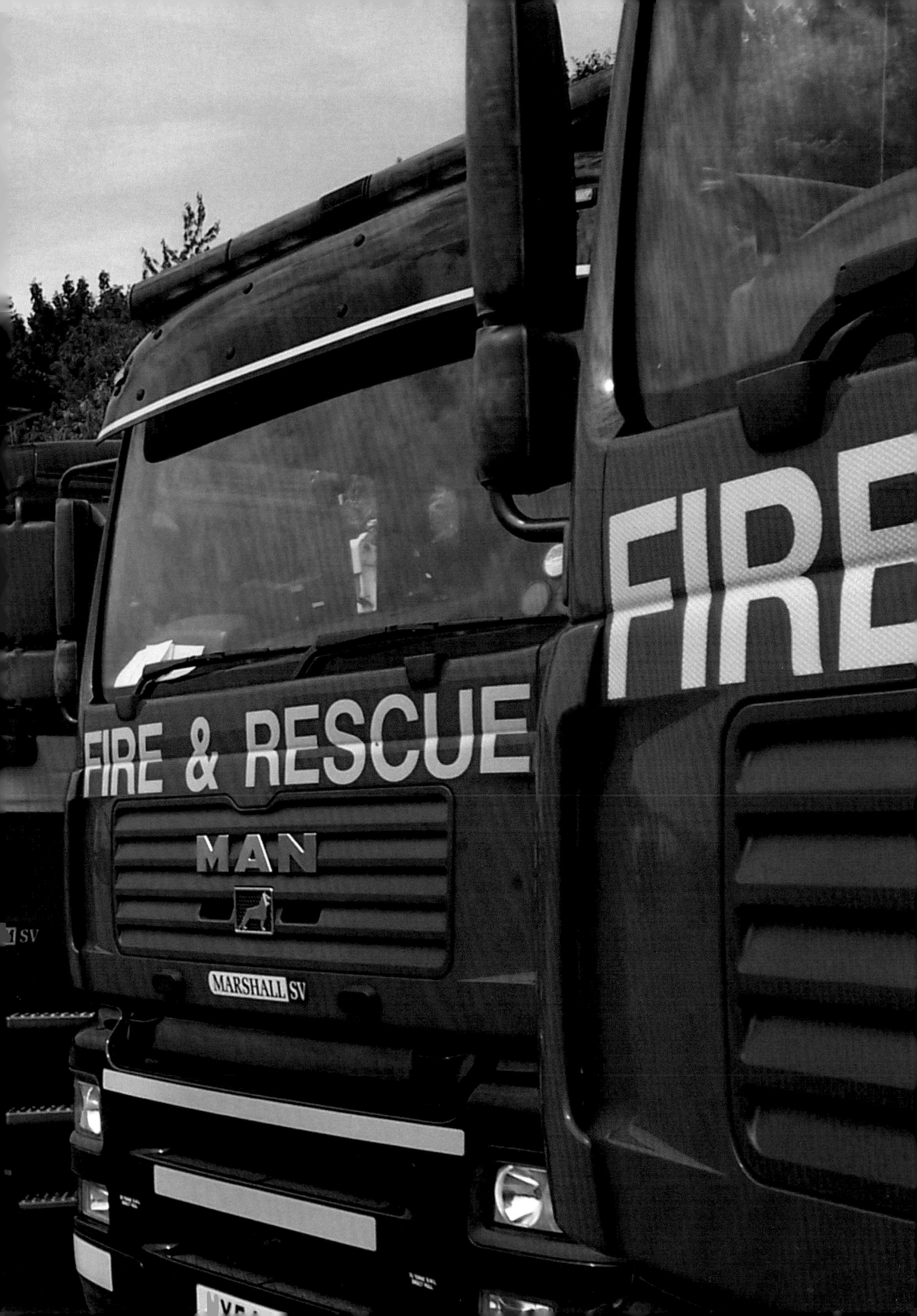
FIRE & RESCUE
MAN
MARSHALL SV
FIRE

This MAN 6 x 4 incident support unit (ISU) provided after September 2001 is attached to Lancashire Fire & Rescue Service and carries a range of decontamination and other equipment. (Lancashire Fire & Rescue Service)

Opposite, top: Another example of the MAN 6 x 4 prime movers is this hazardous materials and environmental protection unit of Lancashire Fire & Rescue Service. (Lancashire Fire & Rescue Service)

Opposite, below: Yet another operational fire and rescue service use of the ubiquitous MAN 6 x 4 prime movers is as a bulk foam carrier. (Lancashire Fire & Rescue Service)

Over page: The operational work of firefighting and rescue crews involves much time spent in a variety of training sessions and scenarios. Here, a crew of recruit firefighters practise a ladder drill at the Severn Park Training Centre, near Bristol. The fire engine being used in the drill is one of several attached to Severn Park and is a MAN chassied water tender (WrT). Severn Park Training Centre is used jointly by Avon, Devon and Somerset, and Gloucestershire Fire & Rescue Services. (Author's collection)

This view shows a demountable high volume pumping set carried on some versions of the MAN prime movers laid out ready to pump water over considerable distances. (Lancashire Fire & Rescue Service)

Opposite, top: Around the turn of the 21st century, a new generation of fire engines utilising plastic bodywork began to appear in several brigades. Lancashire Fire and Rescue Service were one of these pioneer brigades and this 2006 DAF LF55-250 pump ladder (PL) carries a Plastisol body finished by local company TVAC. This fire engine follows over 50 similar such PLs in commission in Lancashire and displays the emerging style of the 21st-century fire engine. (Lancashire Fire & Rescue Service)

Opposite, below: A particularly innovative and unusual new fire engine is this mobile fire station of Lancashire Fire and Rescue Service. Based on a long wheel base Citroen chassis, this vehicle tours the local communities providing free fire safety advice. (Lancashire Fire & Rescue Service)

Three views of a training exercise on Blackpool sea front showing a Lancashire Fire and Rescue Service aerial ladder platform (ALP) being prepared for a rescue scenario involving a high tide. Note the outrigger jacks that are extended to support the considerable forces extended on the chassis of this large fire engine when the booms are extended. (Lancashire Fire & Rescue Service)

A dramatic image of an ERF 6 x 4 foam tender (FoT) of Cheshire Fire and Rescue Service hard at work during firefighting operations at an outbreak in a refinery. Note the effective monitor discharging foam onto the fire and the four lines of delivery hose bringing in the FoT's water supply to be mixed automatically with the on-board foam compound. It is a golden rule in tackling any fire requiring a foam attack on flammable liquids that adequate foam compound supplies must be on hand to sustain a powerful enough firefighting attack that ensures the complete extinguishment of the flames. If the supply of finished foam – foam compound mixed with water and then aerated – runs out before the fire is completely out, there is a considerable danger of violent re-ignition of the flammable liquid. (Cheshire Fire & Rescue Service)

No book about fire engines can ignore the firefighting and rescue teams who crew these impressive vehicles around the clock, in all weathers throughout the year. This view is of firefighters at Farnworth Fire Station of Greater Manchester Fire and Rescue Service proudly posing in front of their brand new 2008 Volvo water tender. This fire engine was one of 16 new Volvos purchased in 2008 by the Greater Manchester Fire Authority at a cost of £2.6 million. The bodies of these new water tenders use lightweight non-corrosive co-polymers in their construction and their engines conform to the latest Euro emission standards. (Greater Manchester Fire & Rescue Service)

In order to minimise likely attendance delays due to heavy urban traffic congestion in peak hour times, Merseyside Fire and Rescue Service have recently introduced several BMW motor cycles as fast response units. These carry fire extinguishers and a minimal amount of other equipment ahead of the main fire engine attendance. (Merseyside Fire & Rescue Service)

In addition to the Merseyside motor cycles, the brigade has also introduced quad bikes to facilitate a first response access to off-road emergency incidents and to areas where access for fire engines might prove initially difficult. (Merseyside Fire & Rescue Service)

Perhaps even more revolutionary is Lancashire Fire and Rescue Service's new 'Softrak' lightweight caterpillar tractor vehicle designed to carry firefighting equipment in off-road operations such as fires involving woods and moorland. (Lancashire Fire & Rescue Service)

This scene depicts the drama of a major fire in East London involving a row of shops with residential properties above. At work from the left are: a Volvo Bronto aerial ladder platform (ALP), a Volvo FL6 pump ladder (PL) and a newer Mercedes PL. This latter fire engine is another example of the increasing use of plastic bodywork, having an Atego cab and Plastisol bodyshell. Since 2002, London Fire Brigade has over 100 such Mercedes pumps in commission with bodyshells mounted by either TVAC or Papworth Specialist Vehicles. (London Fire Brigade)

Acknowledgements

I would firstly like to acknowledge the use of a number of images from individuals utilised throughout this book. These were provided by the late Ron Bentley, Eric Billingham, Jim Bryce, Maurice Cole, Mike Hebard, Jerry Hepworth, Chris Jackson, the late Roger Pennington, S.W. Stevens-Stratten, Keith Wardell and Paul Wood.

In addition, the use of a number of photographs from fire service origins was much appreciated. These include those from London Fire Brigade, Cheshire Fire & Rescue Service, Greater Manchester Fire & Rescue Service, Hampshire Fire & Rescue Service, Kent Fire & Rescue Service, Lancashire Fire & Rescue Service, Merseyside Fire & Rescue Service and Wiltshire Fire & Rescue Service.

I am also honoured to have a Foreword so readily provided by Sir Ken Knight, the government's Chief Fire and Rescue Advisor.

Then I am most grateful for the personal enthusiasm of my publisher, Jeremy Mills, and for the editorial work of Abi Bliss as well as that of the rest of the design and production team at Jeremy Mills Publishing.

Finally, the considerable assistance and support of my wife, Susie, was as with all my books, a key factor in bringing this long-planned title to its conclusion.

Neil Wallington

Further Reading

Blackstone, G.V., *A History of the British Fire Service*, Routledge and Kegan Paul, 1957

Firebrace, Sir Aylmer, *Fire Service Memories*, Andrew Melrose, 1948

Holloway, Sally, *Courage High*, HMSO, 1992

Holloway, Sally and Wallington, Neil, *Fire and Rescue*, Patrick Stephens, 1994

Honeycombe, Gordon, *Red Watch*, Hutchinson, 1976 and Jeremy Mills Publishing, 2007

Ingham, H.S. (editor), *Fire & Water – The London Firefighters' Blitz 1940-42 Remembered*, Firestorm Publications, 1992

Jackson, Eric W., *London's Fire Brigades*, Longmans, 1976

Morris, C.B., *Fire*, Blackie and Son, 1939

Wallington, Neil, *Firemen at War*, Jeremy Mills Publishing, 2007

Wallington, Neil, *Images of Fire*, David & Charles, 1989

Wallington, Neil, *Out of the Flames*, Fire Services National Benevolent Fund, 2003

Wallington, Neil, *In Case of Fire*, Jeremy Mills Publishing, 2005

While, Jack, *Fifty Years of Firefighting in London*, Hutchinson, 1931

Index

The general index is listed first, followed by indexes of fire brigades, fire engine makes, fire stations and manufacturers.
Page numbers in italics refer to picture captions

aerial ladder platform (ALP) 8, 69, 82, 85, *110, 115*
AFS, *see Auxiliary Fire Service*
Air Raid Precautions Act 25
all-terrain vehicles, *see off-road vehicles*
ALP, *see aerial ladder platform*
aluminium bodywork 55, 74, *100*
aluminium extension ladder 44
automatic gearbox 7, 76, 81
Auxiliary Fire Service (AFS) 25-28, *28*, 30-32, 33, 35, 36, 37, 38, 48-52, *54*, 57
aviation firefighting and rescue 55
Battle of Britain 31, 33
Birmingham, bombing of 37
Blitz, the *4, 25*, 31-32, 33-38, 42, *86*
Braidwood, James 78
Braidwood style bodywork 13-14, 17, 18, *19*, 20, 24
breathing apparatus 4, *12*, 14, *36, 50*, 56, 63, 77, 78, 81, 93
British Empire Exhibition 16
caterpillar tractor vehicle 115
centrifugal pumps 11, 12
chemical incidents 77, 93
Chorley 10
City of London bombing 31, 38
Cold War, the 48-49, 51, 52
Coventry, bombing of 36
Daily Mirror 31
demountable operational units 47, 76-77, 93, *101, 108*
denationalisation of the fire service 6, 40
East India Docks 35
Eddington, Superintendent 2
Ellis, the Hon. Evelyn 9
European harmonised standards 42, 82, *112*
fast response units 7, 71, *71, 114*
Fire Brigade Act 1938 25
fire brigade mergers 69
fire engine colour variations 59

Fire Service (Emergency Provisions) Bill 1941 37
Fire Service Technical College (now Fire Service College) *71*
fireboats 34
foam tender 4, *14*, 16, 55, 58, 69, 70, *82, 111*
glass fibre bodywork 7, 74
Guildford 13, 16
Hazardous Material Units 93
high conspicuity liveries 59, 92
HP, *see hydraulic platform*
hydraulic platform 7, 8, 58, *60*, 62, 69, 74, 76, 78, 82, *84*
Jackson, Major Frank 35
JCDD, *see Joint Committee for Design and Development specifications*
Joint Committee for Design and Development specifications (JCDD) 14, 41-42, 70
limousine bodied engines 5, 14, 18, *64*
London Regional Fire Control 34
London taxi cab *25*, 27, 36
London's Burning 78
Loughborough Consultants Ltd 70
Luftwaffe 24, 31, 33, 35-38
Morrison, Herbert, Home Secretary 37
motor cycles *114*
moulded bodywork 92
National Fire Service (NFS) *35*, 37-40, 41, *42*, 48-49
New World bodywork 5, 14, 17, *42*
NFS, see National Fire Service
off-road vehicles 6, 46, 47, 81, *82*, 93, *114, 115*
OHV (overhead valve) engine 17, 20, 45
Pimlico (London) 22
plastic bodywork *108, 115*
quad bikes *114*
red riders 33
rescue tender (RT) 7, *42*, 55, *71*, 72, 81, 93

Riverdale, Lord 25
Royal Arsenal 35
Royal Docks 34
RT, *see rescue tender*
Second World War, *see World War II*
September 11 terrorist attacks 92, *101*
Severn Park Training Centre *104*
Sly, Chief Officer 2
Smithfield Meat Market 56
Southampton, bombing of 37
Spanish Civil War 24
special services 22
steel crew safety cabs 7, 76
Surrey Docks 34-35, 78
Thameshaven fuel depot 31, *32*
TL, *see turntable ladder*
trailer pump 6, 14, 15, 19, 20, *25*, 26, 27, 28, 30, 31, 33, *35*, 35, 41, 42, 49
turntable ladder (TL) 4, 5, 6, 8, 13, 21, 24, 26, 30, 34, *34*, 38, *40*, 41, *42*, 46, 52, 58, 59, 60, 62, *64, 66*, 67, 70, 74, *75*, 77, 78, 80, 82, *86, 91, 94, 95*
V1 and V2 rockets 38-40
West India Docks 31, 35
World War II 11, 60, 66

Fire Brigades:
Avon Fire and Rescue Service *104*
Bedford Fire Brigade 20
Bedfordshire Fire Brigade 58, 59, 71
Bedfordshire Fire and Rescue Service *100*
Belfast Fire Brigade 12
Birmingham Fire and Ambulance Service 45
Birmingham Fire Brigade 17
Bradford Fire Brigade, *see City of Bradford Fire Brigade*
Bristol Fire Brigade, *see City of Bristol Fire Brigade*
Cambridgeshire Fire Brigade 81
Cardiff City Fire Brigade *40, 42*

Central Area Scotland Fire Brigade 52
Cheshire Fire and Rescue Service *111*
Cheshire Fire Brigade *8*
City of Bradford Fire Brigade 3, 11
City of Bristol Fire Brigade 47
City of Nottingham Fire Brigade 13, 54, *68*
City of Sheffield Fire Brigade *67*
Clwyd Fire Brigade 72
Cornwall Fire Brigade 72
County Borough of Hastings Fire Brigade *35, 66*
County of Flint Fire Brigade *40*
County of Flintshire Fire Brigade 69
Coventry Fire Brigade 21, 36, *58*, 59, 92
Croydon Fire Brigade *50*, 69
Darlington Fire Brigade 60
Devon and Somerset Fire and Rescue Service *104*
Dublin Fire Brigade 3, 10
Dublin Fire Department, *see Dublin Fire Brigade*
Durham Fire Brigade 69
East Ham Fire Brigade 69
East Sussex Fire Brigade *66*
Eastbourne County Borough Fire Brigade 47
Eccles Fire Brigade 1, 9
Edinburgh Fire Brigade 14, 17-18
Essex County Fire Brigade 60, *60*, 69
Finchley Fire Brigade *2*, 2-3, 10
Glamorgan Fire Brigade 52
Glasgow Fire Brigade 13, 20, 21
Glasgow Fire Service 60, 65-68
Gloucestershire Fire and Rescue Service *104*
Grampian Fire Brigade 77, 81, *100*
Great Yarmouth Fire Brigade *7*
Greater London Fire Brigade 69
Greater Manchester County Fire Service 76
Greater Manchester Fire and Rescue Service 69, 112
Gwent Fire Brigade 58, 59, *80*
Hampshire Fire and Rescue Service *52*, 69, *77, 100*
Hertfordshire Fire Brigade 69, *71*, 81
Horsham Fire Brigade *19*
Hull City Police Fire Brigade 21
Humberside Fire Brigade 81
Ilford Fire Brigade 21
Isle Of Wight Fire Brigade *45*
Kent Fire Brigade 46, 55, 69, *91*
Kingston-upon-Hull Fire Brigade 52
Kingston-upon-Thames Fire Brigade 13
Lanarkshire Fire Brigade 52
Lancashire County Fire Brigade 69, *85*
Lancashire Fire and Rescue Service *85*, 94, *95, 104, 108, 110, 115*
Liverpool Fire Brigade 1, 9, 54, *60*, 62, 68-69
London Fire Brigade 3, 4, *4*, 9, 11, *11*, 12, *12*, 13, 14, 21, *21*, 22, 24, 25, *25*, 26, 28, 31, 33-4, *34*, 35-6, *36*, 37, *38*, 46, 54, 56, 64, 69, *75, 78*, 80, 81, *81*, *84*, *85*, *86*, *87*, *88*, *91*, 92, 93, *94*, *95*, *115*
Lothian and Borders Fire Brigade 81
Luton Fire Brigade 17, 19
Manchester Fire Brigade 15, 21, 59, 60, 69

Merionethshire County Fire Brigade 47
Merseyside Fire and Rescue Service 69, 93, *114*
Merseyside Fire Brigade *60*, 70-71
Merthyr Tydfil Fire Brigade *5*, *47*
Metropolitan Fire Brigade (London) 9
Mid Glamorgan Fire Service 72, 77
Middlesex Fire Brigade 45, 69
Monmouthshire Fire Brigade 8, 58, 78
Newcastle and Gateshead Joint Fire Service 63, 64
Newcastle Fire Brigade 13
Newport Fire Brigade 59
Norfolk Fire Brigade *7*
Northern Area Fire Brigade (Scotland) 72
Nottingham Fire Brigade, *see City of Nottingham Fire Brigade*
Oakham and Uppingham Joint Fire Brigade 18
Oxfordshire Fire Brigade 76
Princes Risborough Fire Brigade 19
Rangoon Fire Brigade 59
Shanghai Fire Brigade 13
Sheffield Fire Brigade, *see City of Sheffield Fire Brigade*
Somerset Fire Brigade 52, 72
South Eastern Fire Brigade (Scotland) *6*, 52
South Yorkshire Fire Brigade 69, 81
Staffordshire Fire and Rescue Service *101*
Strathclyde Fire Brigade 80, 81
Suffolk Fire Service 77
Sunderland Fire Brigade 72
Surrey Fire Brigade 46, 52, 69, 71, 81
Tottenham Fire Brigade 2, 10
Tyne and Wear Fire Brigade 69
West Ham Fire Brigade 69
West Midlands Fire Brigade 69
West Riding of Yorkshire Fire Brigade 59, 69
West Sussex Fire Brigade 59, 72
West Yorkshire Fire and Rescue Service *iv*
Wiltshire Fire and Rescue Service 84, *90*
Wolverhampton Fire Brigade 60
York Fire Brigade 59

Fire Engine Makes:
AEC Mercury/Merryweather *6*, 52, 59, *67*, *68*, *75*
AEC/Merryweather Regal 52
AEC Regent III/Merryweather *5*, *47*, 52, 64
Albion CX 6
Albion Fire Chief 63
Alvis Salamander 55
Austin Gypsy 51
Austin K2 27, 28, *35*, 37
Austin K4 27-28, 35, 38
Bedford 4 x 4 Mobile Control Unit *54*
Bedford A type 6
Bedford Green Goddess 49-50, 51-52, *52*, 57
Bedford J type 6
Bedford Mark II 19
Bedford S type 6
Bedford SB *50*
Bedford TJ 57
Bedford TK 57, 77

Bedford/HCB Angus *58*
Beresford Stork 28
Bijou 1, 9
Bikini (transportable water unit) 51-52, *54*
Carmichael Cobra *82*
Carmichael Commando *71*, 71-72
Chubb Pacesetter 70
Chubb Pathfinder 72
Commer G16C 80
Commer Karrier Gamecock 6, 54
Commer QX 6, 44
Commer VAC 8, 58, 78
Coventry Climax FSM 28
DAF LF55-250 *108*
Daimler (1901) 1, 9
Dennis (Bradford, 1908) 3
Dennis (Kingston-upon-Thames, 1910) 13
Dennis (London, 1910) 3
Dennis (London, 1919) *12*
Dennis Ace 18
Dennis Big 4 *4*, 18, *20*, 28
Dennis Big 6 18
Dennis D 65, 67
Dennis DS 76
Dennis ET *36*
Dennis F1 43
Dennis F7 6, 43, *46*
Dennis F8 6, 43, 44, *49*, 52, 62
Dennis F12 6, 43, 52, 56, 62, *64*
Dennis F24 *7*, 54
Dennis F25 54
Dennis F26 62
Dennis F44 62
Dennis F45 62
Dennis F49 68
Dennis F101 52, 54, 56, 62
Dennis F102 54, 62
Dennis F106 *87*
Dennis F108 52, 65, 74, *95*
Dennis F109 65, *69*, 74
Dennis F117 *60*, 62
Dennis F123 62, 80
Dennis F125 *60*, 80
Dennis G type 16
Dennis Light 4 43
Dennis New World *5*, 14, 17, *42*
Dennis R 74
Dennis Rapier *82*, *91*
Dennis RS 76, *81*
Dennis Sabre 84, *90*, *91*
Dennis SS 76
Dennis/Alfred Miles F8 *49*
Dodge G13 76
Dodge G1313 80
Dodge G16 76, 80
Dodge K1050 76
Dodge K850 68, 76
ERF 6 x 4 *111*
ERF 64PF 63
ERF 84PS 80
ERF 84RF *8*
ERF/HCB Angus *62*
Ford A 81
Ford D1616 69

Ford D600 63
Fordson 7V *26, 27, 28*, 35
Green Goddess, *see Bedford Green Goddess*
Iveco 82, *91*
Karrier Gamecock, *see Carmichael Karrier Gamecock*
Land Rover Mark I 6
Land Rover Series I 46-47
Leyland (Dublin, 1910) 3
Leyland Atlas 64
Leyland Beaver TSC 38, *40*
Leyland Comet 6, 44, 46, 59
Leyland Firemaster 7, 60, 70
Leyland FK1 17
Leyland FT1 17
Leyland limousine (1936) *64*
Leyland Metz 6, 21, *42*, 86
Leyland New World *42*
Leyland SKFT *42*
Leyland TD7 38
Magirus 13, 21, 30, 58, 60, 64, 65, 66, 80, *91*
MAN 6 x 4 prime mover 92, *101, 104*
Mercedes/Atego 8, 77, 82, *115*
Mercury TGM *66, 67*
Merryweather (Tottenham, 1903) 2, 10
Merryweather AEC Regal, *see AEC/Merryweather Regal*
Merryweather AEC Regent III, *see AEC/Merryweather Regent III*
Merryweather Fire King 1, 10
Merryweather Hatfield *11*, 12
Merryweather Marquis 52
Merryweather XRL 80
Merryweather/Aster (Finchley 1904) 2, 10
Metz 5, 6, 13, 21, 30, *42*, 66, 77, 80, *86*
Morris Magirus 13, 21, *64*
Range Rover Commando, *see Carmichael Commando*
Reynolds Boughton Scorpio 70, 72
Scammell MH6 28
Scania 8, 77, 78, 82, *82, 100, 101*
Scania 124C 420 *82*
Scania 230 94D *100*
Scania 260 94D *100, 101*
Scania LB81 77
Scoosher 67-69
Shelvoke & Drewry 6, 74, 78, 80
Shelvoke and Drewry WY 80
Simon SS *7, 8*, 78, 80
Simon SS65 58, *60*, 62
Simonitor 68, 69
Softrak 93, *115*
Stonefield P5000 81
Thornycroft Mk 5A 55
Thornycroft Nubian 55
Tilling-Stevens/Foamite *14*
Volvo 8, 77, 82, *84, 85, 100, 112, 115*
Volvo Bronto *115*
Volvo FL10 *85*
Volvo FL6 14 *85, 100*
Volvo FL6 18 *84, 85*

Fire Stations:
Bath Street (AFS) (London) *30*

Bedford 58
Birmingham Central *42*
Canley (Coventry) *58*
Clerkenwell (London) *12*
Colchester *60*
Dockhead (London) 78
Euston (London) 35
Farnworth (Greater Manchester) *112*
Hatfield *71*
Garston *71*
Lambeth (London) *28, 46, 94*
Lauriston Place (Edinburgh) *6*
Paddington (London) *88, 95*
Shoreditch (London) *iv*
Soho (London) *86*
Southwark (London) *11*, 35, 78
Stanmore (London) *91*
West Hampstead (London) *75*
Whitechapel (London) 35

Manufacturers and Bodybuilders:
AEC 5, 6, *6*, 30, 43, *47*, 52, 56, 59, 62, *64, 66, 66, 67, 67, 68*, 75, 78, *86, 94*
Albion 4, 6, 11, 14, 18, 20, 21, 44, 65
Alfred Miles 7, 44, *49*, 55
Allison 70, 76
Alvis 55
Angloco 7, 77, 78, *85*
Argyle 4, 11
Aster 2, 10, 11
Austin *25*, 27-28, 35, *35*, 36, 37-38, *42*, 51
Bedford 6, *7*, 19, *19, 20*, 27, 44-45, 48, 49-51, *50, 52, 54*, 55, 57-58, *58*, 59, 62, 63, 67, 71, 74, 77, *77, 100*
Belsize 11
Bennett's 68
Buttons 58
Carmichael 7, 60, 68, *71, 72*, 74, 78, *84*
Carmichael of Worcester 44, 54, 65, 71
Cedes Electric Traction 5
CFE, *see Cheshire Fire Engineering*
Cheshire Fire Engineering 7, *8*, 75
Chevrolet 19
Chubb 70, 72
Citroen *108*
Commer 6, 8, 44, 48, 51, 52, 54, *54*, 55, 58, 62, 63, 78, 80
Commer-Simonis 4, 11
Coventry Climax 28, 47, 50
Daimler 1, 9, 11, 56
David Haydon 7, 60
Dennis 3, 4, 5, 6, 10, 11, 12, *12*, 13, 14, 16, *16*, 17, 18, 20, *22, 25, 28*, 30, 33, *36*, 38, 43-44, 46, *46*, 48, *49*, 52, 54, 56, 57, 60, *60*, 62, 64, 65, 66, 67, 68, *69*, 74-75, 76, 80, *81*, 82, 84, *87, 90, 91, 95*
Dennis Brothers, *see Dennis*
Dodge 6, 38, 44, *45*, 67, 68, 74, 76, 80
Emergency One *100, 101*
ERF 6, *8*, 62, 63, 67, 72, 74, 75, 80, *111*
Ford 6, 26, 27, 28, 30, 63, 67, 69, 74, 77, 81
Fordson 6, *26*, 27, 28, *30*, 35, 38
Girling 76
Gwynne-Sargent 3

Halley Motors 4, 11, 20
Hampshire Car Bodies 7, *7*, 44, *45*, 55, 57, 58, *62*, 63, 68, 69, 80
Harrington 50
HCB, *see Hampshire Car Bodies*
HCB-Angus 7, *58, 62*, 63, *68, 69, 80*
Iveco 82, *91*
Jaguar 65
James Whitson 7, 55
John Dennis Coachbuilders 82, 84, *90*
John Kerr & Company 20
John Morris 4, 7, 20, 21
Karrier Motors 6, 54, 62
Kelly 11
Land Rover 6, 46-47, 51, 63, 71
Leyland 3, 4, 5, 6, 7, 10, 11, 12, 13, 17, 18, 21, 27, 28, 33, 38, *40, 42*, 44, 45, 46, 48, 56, 59, 60, 63, 64, 66, 67, 70, 75, *86, 95*
Magirus 13, 21, 30, 58, 60, 64, 65, 66, 80, *91*
MAN 8, 92, *101, 104, 108*
Mather & Platt 10
Mercedes/Atego 8, 77, 82, *115*
Merryweather 1, *2*, 2-3, 4, 5, *5*, 8, 9, 10-11, *11*, 12, 13, 14, 16, 17, 18, 21, 24, 30, 38, 43, 44, *47*, 52, 56, 58, 59, 62, *64*, 66, *66, 66, 67*, 75, 80, *94*
Metz 5, 6, 13, 21, 30, *42*, 66, 77, 80, *86*
Morris 13, 20, 21, 27, *30, 64*
Ogle 76
Papworth Specialist Vehicles 115
Park Royal 50
Perkins 63, 65, 74-76
Plaxton 50
Powell Duffryn 77
Pyrene 55
Range Rover 7, *71*, 71-72
Rees 17
Reynolds 70, 72
Rolls Royce 43, *46*, 52, 54, 55, 62, 63, 65
Saxon Sanbec Ltd 75, 78
Saxon SVB 75
Scammell 20, 28, 30
Scania 8, 77, 78, 82, *82, 100, 101*
Shand Mason 1, 11, 24
Shelvoke & Drewry 6, 74, 78, 80
Sigmund 50, 60
Simon 7, 8, 58, *60*, 62, 67, 68, 76, 78, 80, *84, 85*
Standard-Triumph 64
Stonefield 81
Sulzer *26, 27*
Sun Engineering 55
Tamini 12
Tangye 27
Thornycroft 20, 55
Tilling-Stevens 11, 13, *14*
TVAC *108, 115*
Volvo 8, 77, 82, *84, 85, 100, 112, 115*
Weymann 50
White & Poppe 3, 11
Willowbrook 50
Wilsden 7
Wilsdon & Co 45, 60
Wolseley 30